EXMOOR GEOLOGY

Exploring the Landscapes, Rocks and Mines of the NATIONAL PARK

R. A. EDWARDS

Supported by

First published in Great Britain in 2000

British Library Cataloguing-in-Publication Data
A CIP record for this title is available from the British Library

ISBN 0 86183 411 9

EXMOOR BOOKS
Official Publisher to the Exmoor National Park Authority

Halsgrove House
Lower Moor Way
Tiverton, Devon EX16 6SS
Tel: 01884 243242
Fax: 01884 243325
www.halsgrove.com

Printed and bound by
The Cromwell Press, Trowbridge, Wiltshire.

Contents

Chapter 1
INTRODUCTION

I have tried in this short book to give you a gentle and enjoyable introduction to the rocks and scenery of Exmoor National Park. As you walk along its beautiful coastline you might wonder about some curious structure that you see in the rocks of the cliffs, or while up on the moors you might spot signs of old mines, or wonder why Exmoor forms a high plateau. I hope to satisfy your curiosity about these and many other features of the rocks and landscape of the area.

The book is certainly not intended to be hard work, and you don't need any special knowledge of geology to read it – just an interest and curiosity in your natural surroundings. It's the sort of book that you might use while on holiday and which might add some extra interest to the walks or excursions that you have planned. It is not (thank goodness!), a geology textbook, and I have avoided geological terms where possible. Those that are necessary are printed in **bold** type and explained (with pronunciations in some cases) in the glossary at the end of the book.

My own interest in Exmoor comes from my work with the British Geological Survey. I was lucky enough during 1993-4 to spend some time making the official geological map of part of eastern Exmoor, which has some of the best and most varied landscapes of the National Park. I found the contrast in scenery between the high moorland, the fertile Vale of Porlock, and the wild and lonely coastline an irresistible combination in such a small and intimate area. Afterwards, while writing a description of the geology, I found that there were plenty of books about the history, wildlife, everyday life and other aspects of Exmoor, but none giving a simple account for the visitor of the rocks and landscape of the National Park as a whole. I have written most of the book from my personal knowledge of Exmoor, but I have also got valuable help by reading and learning from the work of other writers. It is not possible in a book like this to acknowledge in detail all these writers, but I thank them all for their help. Some of the books and articles that I used are listed in the `Further Reading' section at the end of the book, so that if you want to follow up any particular topic in more detail you can easily do so.

The best and most enjoyable way to explore the geology and landscape of any area is to go and look first hand at its rocks and scenery. Following this principle, the heart of this book is made up of series of walks and visits to places where the rocks and landscape can be best explored. Exmoor is such a beautiful place that most of the walks and visits are worth while in their own right, so that the opportunity to add extra interest by looking at the rocks and landscapes is a bonus.

ABOUT THE NATIONAL PARK

The map (Figure 1 on page 17) shows our area of interest – Exmoor National Park. I have shown its boundary and the names of the main places of interest, including rivers. I have also drawn on some height contours which give a rough idea of the shape of the area. The National Park extends along the coast of north Devon and west Somerset for about 34 miles between Combe Martin in the west and Minehead in the east, and goes inland for about 12 miles to Dulverton, the headquarters of the Exmoor National Park Authority. About two-thirds of it is in Somerset and one-third in Devon.

Although Exmoor is one of the smallest (at 267 square miles) of England's National Parks, packed into it are some of the most varied and attractive landscapes that you will find anywhere in Britain. In it are great contrasts of scenery, including rocky coasts, high heather moorland, steep wooded combes, fertile vales, and broad coastal flats. To many people these contrasts are the very essence of Exmoor. The dramatic coastline that forms the northern boundary of the Park is rich in physical and geological interest, and it was one of the reasons why it became a National Park in 1954. Exmoor is an important place for scientists, because large areas of it, both along the coast and inland, are Sites of Special Scientific Interest. These were set up to give some protection to areas which are of importance because of their plant life, wildlife, geology or landscape.

At the heart of the National Park lies the ancient Royal Forest of Exmoor, centred on the village of Simonsbath (pronounced 'Simmunsbath'). It was sold off in 1818 to the Knight family, whose efforts in the nineteenth century to reclaim it for agriculture and to start up iron mines make an interesting story. We shall come across evidence of their attempts to wrest mineral wealth from the moor later in the book. If you are interested in reading more about the Forest and the Knights, I have given the titles of some books in the Further Reading section at the end of the book.

WHAT MAPS TO USE

The Ordnance Survey produce an excellent map of Exmoor in their 1:25 000-scale (2½ inches to the mile) Outdoor Leisure Series (No.9). This is invaluable for walkers, and is highly recommended for use when following the walks in this book. The Ordnance Survey also sell a one-inch to the mile Tourist Map of Exmoor which is handy when you want a less detailed map.

The 1:50 000-scale geological maps of the British Geological Survey are well worth a look if you are interested in more details of the geology. The National Park is covered by four of these 1:50 000 sheets: 277 (Ilfracombe), 278 (Minehead), 293 (Barnstaple) and 294 (Dulverton). Much more about the geology of Exmoor can be found in the Memoirs of the Geological Survey. One is available for the Ilfracombe/Barnstaple area, and another, for the Minehead area, was published in 1999.

ACKNOWLEDGEMENTS

A financial contribution from English Nature is gratefully acknowledged. My thanks go to the British Geological Survey (B.G.S.) for permission to use photographs and the geological maps which form the basis of Figure 2. I am grateful to Hugh Prudden for reading the manuscript and suggesting improvements, and for allowing me to use some of his photographs. He also kindly provided details of localities at Dunkery Gate and County Gate to Malmsmead. Brian Pearce of Exmoor National Park Authority (ENPA) also read and commented on a draft of the book. I am grateful to ENPA for permission to use excerpts from their *Walks from Combe Martin. Silver Mines* leaflet.

Denis Parsons and Andy King of English Nature have kindly contributed the section on conservation (p.83).

The views expressed in this book are those of the author, not of the British Geological Survey or of the Exmoor National Park Authority.

Words in bold are explained in the Glossary, pages 85-92.
B.G.S. = British Geological Survey.

Chapter 2
THE STORY OF EXMOOR'S ROCKS

The history of the landscapes and rocks of our area goes back in time for over 400 million years, to near the beginning of the period which geologists have named the **Devonian**. Even older rocks lie concealed at depth. As in all landscapes, the characters of the rocks and the structures affecting them make up the building blocks of the landscape, but much of the modern shape of Exmoor is the result of later shaping of the landscape by erosion over the last 20 million years. In the last few thousand years, the most obvious changes to the detailed appearance of the landscape of Exmoor have been caused by man. I have not dealt with these man-made influences on the landscape in detail in this book, except in the case of mining and quarrying, where man's activities are closely linked to the rocks. If you are interested in man's effect on the Exmoor landscape, I have listed several books dealing with this topic in the Further Reading section (page 93).

Before we begin to find out more about the rocks of Exmoor and the story that they tell, we need to find out how old they are compared to rocks in other parts of the world.

A LOOK AT GEOLOGICAL TIME

The earth is incredibly ancient – possibly over 4.6 billion years old. Geologists often talk easily about time spans of tens or hundreds of millions of years, but, if they are honest, many of them find it just as difficult as the next person to conceive such vast spans of time.

Before about 570 million years age, there was plenty of life around the world, but it was not easily preserved and few fossils are found in rocks of this age (called **Precambrian**). At about 570 million years, there was a remarkable 'explosion' in the number of easily preserved shelly animals, now preserved as fossils in the rocks. The span of time from 570 million years ago is divided up into parcels of time with special names. This **geological time scale**, with the specially named periods of time, is shown on page 9. The periods are sometimes called after places where the rocks were first studied or are best displayed (a familiar example is the **Jurassic** – an age of dinosaurs – which is named after the Jura mountains in France), or sometimes after some special character of the rocks (an example is the **Carboniferous**, named from the fact that the rocks contain coal [carbon] seams). A lot of the work in sorting out the details of the geological time scale was done by British geologists in the last century, and as a result, several geological periods are named after places in Britain. Of special meaning for us in our exploration of the rocks of Exmoor is the period called the **Devonian**. This was named after the county in

1839 by the geological pioneers Adam Sedgwick and Roderick Murchison.

The Geological Time Scale

Era	Period	Epoch	Age (millions of years)
	Quaternary	Holocene*	0.01
		Pleistocene*	2
	Neogene	Pliocene	6
Cainozoic		Miocene	23
		Oligocene	34
	Palaeogene	Eocene	53
		Palaeocene	65
	Cretaceous		135
Mesozic	Jurassic*		205
	Triassic*		251
	Permian		298
	Carboniferous*		355
Palaeozoic	Devonian*		405
	Silurian		435
	Ordovician		510
	Cambrian		570
Precambrian – to the beginning of the Earth (about 4.6 billion years ago)			4600

* Rocks of this age are found on Exmoor

Now that we have some idea of the time scale involved, we can see where Exmoor's rocks fit into it. Most of the rocks on Exmoor are between 405 and 355 million years old and therefore belong to the **Devonian**. On the eastern side of the Park, around Porlock and Minehead, are rocks which are of **Triassic** and **Jurassic** age. Then there are a variety of much younger deposits which formed in the last two million years and which therefore belong to the **Quaternary**. You can identify these names and ages on the geological time scale to the left.

The sorts of rocks that underlie Exmoor are very different from those beneath its sister National Park, Dartmoor, to the south. The rocks of Exmoor are made up of fragments of varying sizes which were worn off pre-existing rocks and then were laid down in water or on land to form layers that were eventually cemented to form rock. These are called **sedimentary** rocks. Dartmoor, on the other hand, is made of **granite**, which was originally a mass of molten rock that formed crystals when it cooled down. This type of rock is called **igneous**.

DIFFERENT TYPES OF ROCK

This is a good place to describe briefly the main kinds of rocks that occur on Exmoor. Most of the sedimentary rocks there are cemented-together versions of material that was originally laid down as loose fragments. So:

- Gravels become stuck together to form **conglomerate**
- **Screes** or **fans** of angular rock fragments become the curiously named **breccia**
- Sand is cemented to form **sandstone**
- Mud is transformed into **mudstone** or **shale** (shales split more easily than mudstones)
- Limy deposits are hardened into **limestone**.

All these kinds of rock are found on Exmoor.

Another important rock on Exmoor is **slate**. The important thing about slates is that they split easily into thin sheets along weaknesses in the rock called

cleavage. The cleavage formed by intense squashing, deep in the earth's crust, of what were originally muds. This caused the fine-grained 'platy' minerals in the rock to align and form planes of weakness along which splitting can take place.

The small scale layers that are found in sedimentary rocks are called **beds**, and these are the most obvious layers that you will see when you look at sandstone cliffs. However, when you look at slates in the cliffs, the most obvious layers that you see are usually cleavage rather than the original beds. Cleavage can be so strong that it can almost completely obliterate any signs of the original beds.

TWO THINGS ABOUT LAYERED ROCKS

There are a couple of useful points to make about layered (**sedimentary**) rocks, amongst which are included our **Devonian** rocks.

The first point is that when these types of rocks were first formed their layers were more or less flat-lying. What generally happens later, however, is that the rocks are tilted, bent and cracked by earth movements, so the layers that we generally now see in cliffs and quarries are tilted and bent, and anything but flat-lying.

The second point is that, in a pile of layered rocks, the lower layers formed first and are therefore the oldest. This piece of common sense is an important principle in understanding layered rocks. It is true in most cases, but can come a bit unstuck when whole chunks of rock have been turned upside down, for example by earth movements.

DEVONIAN ROCKS – SANDSTONE AND SLATE

As I said briefly above, most of Exmoor is made up of **Devonian** rocks, 405 to 355 million years old. They occur in thick (several hundred metres) layers (or **formations**) which are made up either mainly of sandstone or mainly of slate. Each formation is given a name usually made up of the place where it is best seen, plus a rock name which gives some idea of the main sort of rock making up the formation (either sandstone or slate). The rock name may be a bit of a simplification since each formation can include other sorts of rock. For example, the **Hangman Sandstone**, (see the box below) although mainly made up **sandstone**, also includes some **shale** and **slate**. Also, the **Ilfracombe Slates** include some **limestone**.

The Devonian formations of Exmoor, their names, thicknesses, and brief descriptions of the main types of rock, are summarised in the box below. The names are in order from the oldest at the bottom to youngest at the top.

Devonian Formations of Exmoor

Formation	Thickness
Pilton Shales: Shales with sandstones	350 m
Baggy Sandstones: Sandstones, siltstones and shales	450 m
Upcott Slates: Buff, green and purple slates	250 m
Pickwell Down Sandstones: Purple and brown sandstones with shales	1200 m
Morte Slates: Grey slates	1500 m
Ilfracombe Slates: Slates, sandstones, limestones	545 m
Hangman Sandstone: Purple, grey and green sandstones with slate, mudstone and conglomerate	1660 m
Lynton Formation: Slates, siltstones and sandstones	350 m

GEOLOGICAL STUDIES OF EXMOOR

Geological studies of Exmoor began with the pioneer work of Leonard Horner, published in 1816, the year after the Battle of Waterloo. This work included a hand-coloured map of West Somerset, showing for the first time major divisions of the rocks. **Devonian** rocks ('Grauwacke'), **Triassic** ('Conglomerates, Sandstones, Red Rock etc.') and **Jurassic** rocks ('Lyas Strata') were distinguished, and some **Quaternary** deposits ('Marsh and Alluvial Land') were also shown. Since Horner's time, many more detailed studies of various aspects of Exmoor geology have been produced. The earliest Geological Survey maps of Exmoor, on the scale of one-inch to the mile, were produced in the 1830s. In the 1970s the Survey turned its attention to producing modern maps of western Exmoor based on surveys at the 6-inches to the mile scale. Most recently, the Survey has completed geological mapping of a neglected part of eastern Exmoor between County Gate and Minehead, for which there has never been a published modern geological map.

THE GEOLOGICAL MAP OF EXMOOR

If you look at the geological map (Figure 2) on page 18, you can make out the present-day arrangement of the Devonian rocks. You can trace each formation across Exmoor as a series of stripe-like bands which cross the moor in a roughly east to west direction. What has happened is that the thick pile of Devonian rocks, originally flat-lying when formed, have been bent by earth movements (about 300 million years ago) into a large arch-like structure which geologists call an **anticline**. The centre of the arch runs eastwards from Lynton towards Porlock. North of the arch the rocks are generally tilted northwards; south of it and so over most of Exmoor, the tilt is generally to the south. The oldest of the Devonian rocks (the **Lynton Formation**) occur in the centre of the anticline, and successively younger rocks are present the farther south we go. However, in the Brayford area in the south-west of the National Park, there is a reversal of the generally southerly dip, and the rocks there are involved in a **syncline**, in which the beds dip inwards. The general southerly dip is, however, resumed again south of the syncline. You can understand better what has happened by looking at the cross-sections across Exmoor shown on p.19.

Of the Devonian formations listed in the box on page 10, you can see the lowest three – the **Lynton Formation, Hangman Sandstone**, and **Ilfracombe Slates** – in the cliffs of the National Park. The rest – the **Morte Slates, Pickwell Down Sandstones, Upcott Slates, Baggy Sandstones** and **Pilton Shales** – are only found in the inland part of the National Park, but west of the Park they can be seen in the cliffs between Mortehoe and Croyde. Away from the cliffs it is not all that common to see rocks at the surface because they are usually hidden under soil or a cover of Quaternary deposits, for example, **head, alluvium, peat** etc. (for more about these deposits, see pages 16-21). Sometimes they do emerge, in the beds of rivers or as crags on valley sides, in old quarries, or in track and road cuttings. There is no doubt that the coast is the best place to go to look at any of these rocks in detail.

FOSSILS

Fossils present in the Devonian rocks of Exmoor are important for helping to understand the conditions in which the rocks were laid down. For example, the **corals** found in the limestones of the **Ilfracombe Slates** suggest that they were formed in fairly shallow warm clear seas. Those rocks that were formed on land – mainly sandstones like the Hangman Sandstone – do not by their nature contain many fossils. A few plant fragments and remains of fish have been found, but they are very rare. The **Pickwell Down Sandstones** contain interesting examples of very early land plants. Some fossil sea shells do occur in the youngest part of the Hangman Sandstone where the influence of the sea was beginning to be felt.

Because they were formed in the sea, the more slaty formations – like the **Ilfracombe Slates** and **Lynton Formation** – contain more fossils. These include **bivalves, brachiopods** and **crinoids** (sea-lilies). In places they are rather poorly preserved, or have been deformed by the cleavage. In the Ilfracombe Slates, almost all the fossils have been found in the limestones, and include especially **corals**. Apart from the fossil remains of the animals or plants themselves, there are other kinds of 'fossil'. These consist of the traces that the animal has left in the rocks, while the animal itself is not preserved. The best example of this kind of fossil is *Chondrites* (kon-dry-tees) which is found in the Lynton Formation and also in the Ilfracombe Slates (see Plate 1). This **trace-fossil** is mainly found in slates and consists of branching tubes filled with sandstone, probably made by a burrowing worm.

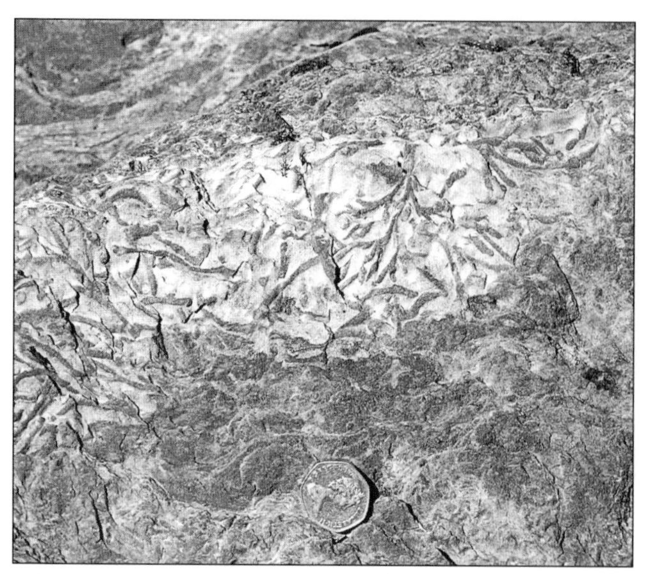

Plate 1. *The trace-fossil* Chondrites, *made by a burrowing worm, found in the Ilfracombe Slates at Combe Martin.*

DEVONIAN RIVERS AND SEAS (405 TO 355 MILLION YEARS AGO)

About 400 million years ago, Britain lay about 10° south of the equator and the climate was much warmer than it is now. Since then, the continents have moved about on the face of the earth. The story of the Devonian landscape in our area is the story of a long battle between land and sea. South Wales was dry land, part of a large desert continent, while at the same time a shallow tropical sea with coral reefs covered South Devon. The continent to the north is sometimes called the 'Old Red Sandstone' continent because the sandstones that formed on it are mainly red owing to oxidation of the iron compounds in the hot desert. Exmoor lay between the two areas, and the shoreline between the continent to the north and the sea to the south was continually changing its position. At times, it lay far to the south and Exmoor was the site of a sandy plain across which rivers flowed south to the sea. This was the situation during formation of the Hangman Sandstone and the Pickwell Down Sandstone, which are of 'Old Red Sandstone' type. At other times, the sea pushed farther north and the shoreline lay north of Exmoor. During these episodes, Exmoor was the site of a shallow sea, for example during the formation of the Lynton, Ilfracombe and Morte slates.

Photo courtesy of Mr H. C. Prudden.

Plate 2. *A fold (anticline) in the Hangman Sandstone at Greenaleigh, west of Minehead.*

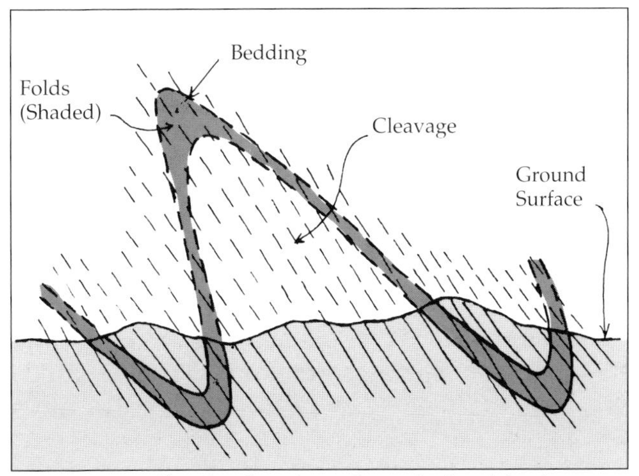

Figure 3. *Sketch showing the relationship between bedding, cleavage and folds. See Plate 44 for actual examples near Combe Martin.*

THE GREAT UPHEAVAL

About 300 million years ago, the scene was rudely interrupted by great mountain-building earth movements. The flat-lying Devonian and Carboniferous rocks were squashed, as in a vice, by powerful north-south compression which forced the rocks to crack and buckle (**fold**), like a carpet being rucked up (Plate 2). The strong squeezing led to the widespread formation of large and small folds trending generally east-west, as well as cracks in the rocks (**faults**) and **cleavage**. The relationships between **bedding, cleavage** and **folds** is shown in the sketch (Figure 3). Veins of white **quartz** filled cracks in the rocks and are common in places (Plate 3).

As a result of these tremendous forces, a chain of mountains rose over South-West England. We can only guess at the eventual height of these mountains, but they may have been as high as the Himalayas.

Plate 3. *Quartz veins in the Ilfracombe Slates near Lester Point, Combe Martin.*

What we now see are the worn-down stumps of the mountains.

I have already described (on page 11) the effects of the earth movements on the Devonian formations of Exmoor, which were to bend them into a large arch-like structure or **anticline**.

Although the broad surface structure of the geological formations of Exmoor is fairly simple, it is very complicated in detail. One of the most immediate things that will strike your eye when you come to look at the cliffs of Exmoor is the extent to which the Devonian rocks are affected by folds and faults.

CRACKS IN THE ROCKS

Faults are cracks in the earth's crust along which rocks have moved relative to each other. Several large faults affect the rocks of Exmoor as well as many minor ones. I have shown some of the big faults on the geological map (Figure 2). The most important ones are: the fault along the Combe Martin valley; the fault between Little Hangman and Parracombe; the fault between Lynmouth and Malmsmead; the east-west Brushford Fault which effectively defines the southern physical edge of Exmoor; and the Timberscombe Fault in eastern Exmoor.

The valleys of Porlock Vale and Minehead have big faults along their north sides. These have allowed the red rocks filling the valleys to subside like a trapdoor with its hinge along the south side of the valleys. So, the rocks are all tilted northwards and are thickest on the north side of the valleys.

RED ROCKS – THE TRIASSIC (251-205 MILLION YEARS)

After the mountain building episode which I have described above, a great change occurred in the types of rocks formed on Exmoor, as the **Triassic** period began. The great mountain chain began to be worn down, from about 300 million years ago, and huge amounts of gravel, sand and clay were washed down into the surrounding valleys and plains. The climate was semi-desert and most of the rocks are 'rusted' to red colours. You can see from the geological map (Figure 2, page 18) that these Triassic red rocks appear on the eastern side of the National Park, around Porlock, Luccombe, Wootton Courtenay and Minehead. They are called '**New Red Sandstone**' in contrast to the Devonian 'Old Red Sandstone'. These rocks don't contain obvious fossils, but microscopic plant fossils have been found in some places.

As far as the National Park is concerned, the first rocks were laid down around Luccombe in the Vale of Porlock, as gravel **fans** spreading out from the mountains. These are the **Luccombe Breccias**, which are a kind of ancient gravel mainly made up of small pieces of sandstone and slate. Their sharp edges show that they have not travelled far enough to be worn smooth. In contrast, there are beds of round boulders which must have travelled farther to be worn so round (see Plate 4). They may have formed in a river channel. You can see these 'Boulder Beds' near Luccombe (see Places To Go, page 51). There is no Luccombe Breccia around Minehead. Instead, there are red **sandstones** such as those in Holloway Street (Plate 5) (see Places To Go, page 44) and **conglomerates** such as those at Alcombe Quarry south of Minehead. These Alcombe conglomerates may correspond with the **Budleigh Salterton Pebble Beds** found near the town of that

Photo courtesy of B.G.S.

Plate 4. *The 'Boulder Bed' in Huish Ball Steep, near Luccombe.*

name on the south coast of Devon. The Alcombe conglomerates contain large pebbles and boulders of rounded **limestone** which were probably moved by ancient rivers flowing from South Wales or the Mendips. The quarry workers last century picked out the limestone pebbles from the conglomerate and burnt them in kilns to make lime.

When the mountains had been well worn down, there followed a quieter time when red mud was laid down over a wide area, probably in a semi-desert climate, on mudflats and in lakes. These muds, now hardened to **mudstones**, are called the **Mercia Mudstone**. They fill up a large part of Porlock Vale, forming the low ground between the hills of Devonian sandstone to north and south of the valley. They also occur beneath most of the lower part of Minehead town and beneath the coastal flats east of Minehead.

Towards the top of the Mercia Mudstone, there is a change to grey and green mudstones, the **Blue Anchor Formation**, and then black shales and limestones, the **Penarth Group**, formerly called the 'Rhaetic' (Ree-tick). These rocks show the influence of the sea which at that time (about 210 million years ago) was gradually invading the land from the south. There are no good places in the National Park to see these rocks, but they form the wooded ridge which you can see to the north of the A39 road as you approach the Selworthy turn-off from the east. If you are interested in seeing the Blue Anchor Formation and Penarth Group in more detail, they are splendidly displayed in the cliffs and foreshore at Blue Anchor, east of the National Park.

JURASSIC SEAS (205-195 MILLION YEARS)

Jurassic rocks are found in the National Park only near Selworthy. They are grey shales with thin layers of limestone, formed in a shallow tropical sea. They are often referred to as '**Blue Lias**', famously developed at Lyme Regis on the Dorset coast and also on the coast between Blue Anchor and Watchet (outside the National Park). You cannot see them easily near Selworthy, and you will need to go to the coast if you want to see them properly. They contain fossils, especially **ammonites** and **bivalves**.

THE LAST TWO MILLION YEARS – THE ICE AGE AND AFTERWARDS

The youngest 'solid' rocks left on Exmoor belong to the lower part of the Jurassic, and are about 195 million years old. You can see from a look at the geological timescale on page 9 that there is an immense gap of time, about 193 million years, before the formation of the **Quaternary** deposits from about two million years ago, for which no rocks are now preserved on Exmoor. This is not to say that rocks of the missing periods – the middle and upper parts of the **Jurassic, Cretaceous**, and **Tertiary** – were never present on Exmoor, for its seems highly likely, for example, that about 90 million years ago a tropical sea submerged Exmoor and on its bed **Chalk** was laid down.

The last two million years were a time of tremendous changes in the climate of Britain. Great **ice sheets** advanced from the north at least three times and then retreated. Between these periods of severe cold, collectively called the **Ice Age**, the climate became at times as warm or even warmer than today. In one of these '**interglacial**' periods, for example, luxuriant forests spread over Britain, and hippopotamus lived as far north as Yorkshire! Then, about 10, 000 years ago, the last ice sheet melted and the climate became more temperate. Of course, there is no way of telling whether the Ice Age is really over, or whether we are within yet another interglacial period!

During the Ice Age, Exmoor probably lay just south of the ice sheets. It is even possible that the next to last ice sheet actually pressed right up against the cliffs of Exmoor. The nearness of the ice sheets had a tremendous effect on the deposits and landscape of the area. One of the most widespread of the Quaternary deposits is called '**head**' and consists of clay with angular pieces of local rock. These head deposits probably formed during a cold period of the Ice Age. Then, alternate freezing and thawing of surface layers resulted in waterlogged soil and other material which moved like porridge down slopes.

Generally, head occurs just about everywhere on Exmoor, forming a kind of skin over most of the Devonian rocks, but it may be missing on steep slopes and on higher ground. You can see it in just about any small quarry or cutting. It can be very thick in places, for example up to 200ft (60m) are present beneath the floor of the Valley of Rocks near Lynton (described on page 61). In Porlock Vale, the head forms a sloping area at the foot of the steeper Devonian slopes between Porlock Weir and Porlock, and it can be seen where the sea has cut low cliffs in it at Porlock Beach, near Porlock Weir (shown in Plate 6).

No one has yet found any definite glacial deposits on Exmoor, and there is no way of knowing for sure whether there was a small **ice cap** on Exmoor at some time during the Ice Age, although it seems quite likely. Some geologists have suggested that the deeply cut valley of the River Bray just west of the Park may have been a channel cut by water released when an ice cap melted. Professor Straw has recently put forward the interesting idea that The Punchbowl [SS 882 344] (Plate 7), a distinctive bowl-shaped hollow on the north-east side of Winsford Hill (see Places to Go, page 82), may have been an incipient **glacial corrie** – that is,

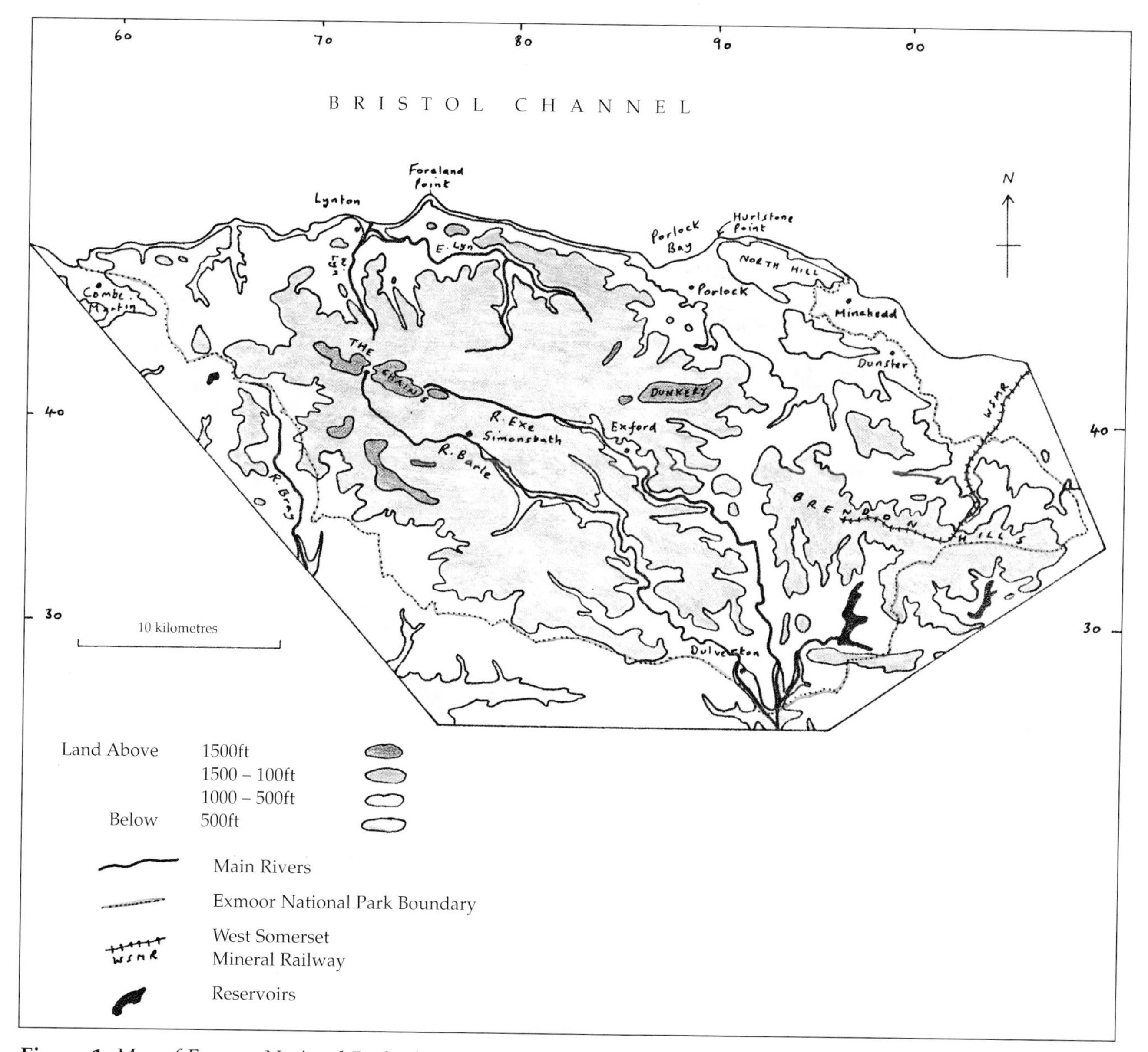

Figure 1. *Map of Exmoor National Park, showing physical features, rivers, main towns etc.*

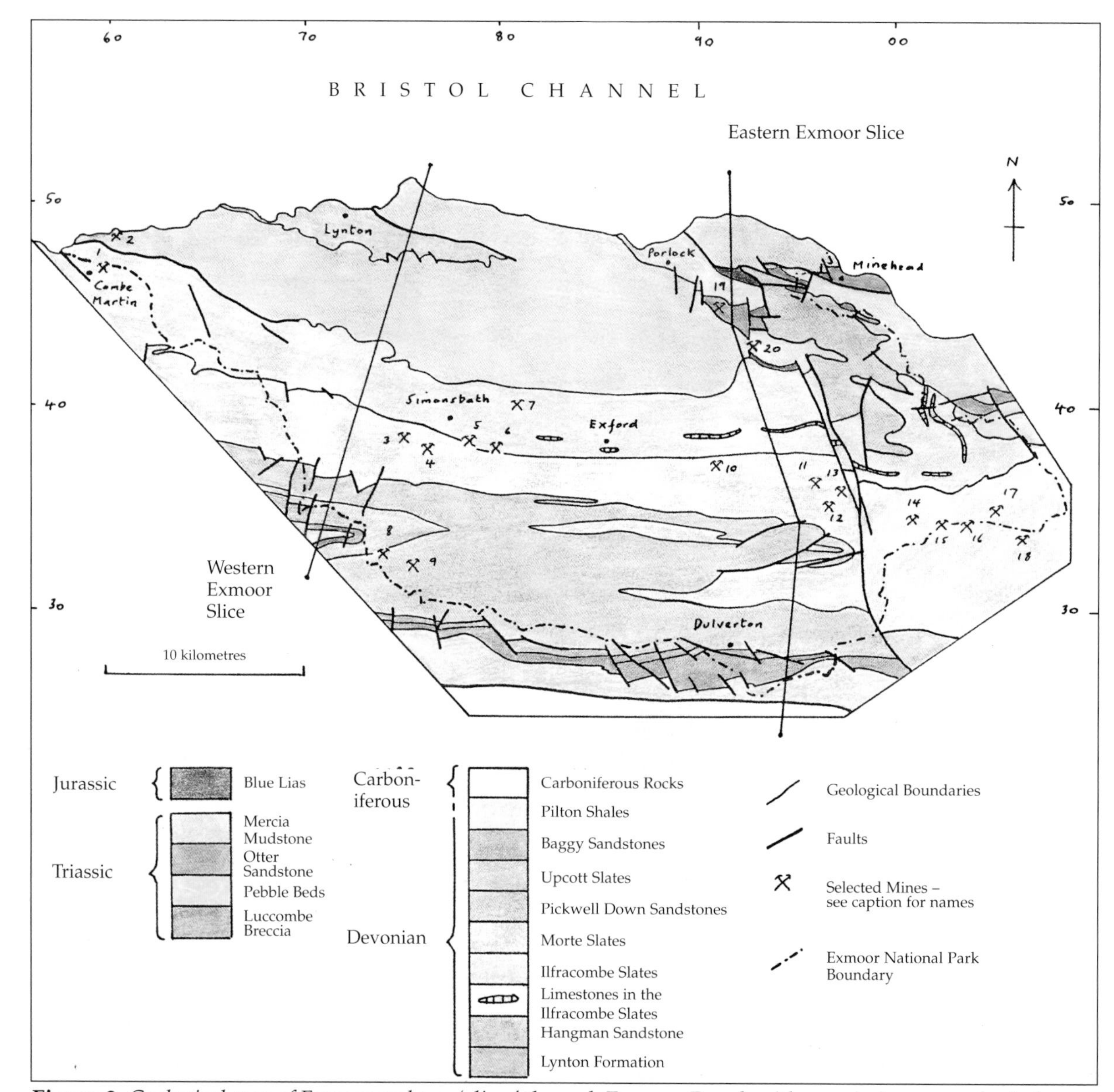

Figure 2. *Geological map of Exmoor and two 'slices' through Exmoor. Based, with permission, on geological maps of the British Geological Survey.*
1 Combe Martin, 2 Blackstone Point, 3 Deerpark, 4 Exmoor, 5 Wheal Eliza, 6 Picked Stones, 7 Honeymead, 8 Bampfylde, 9 Florence, 10 Eisen Hill, 11 Kennisham Hill, 12 Gupworthy, 13 Bearland Wood, 14 Burrow Farm, 15 Carnarvon and Raleigh's Cross, 16 Carew, 17 Colton, 18 Yeanon, 19 Luccombe, 20 Brockwell

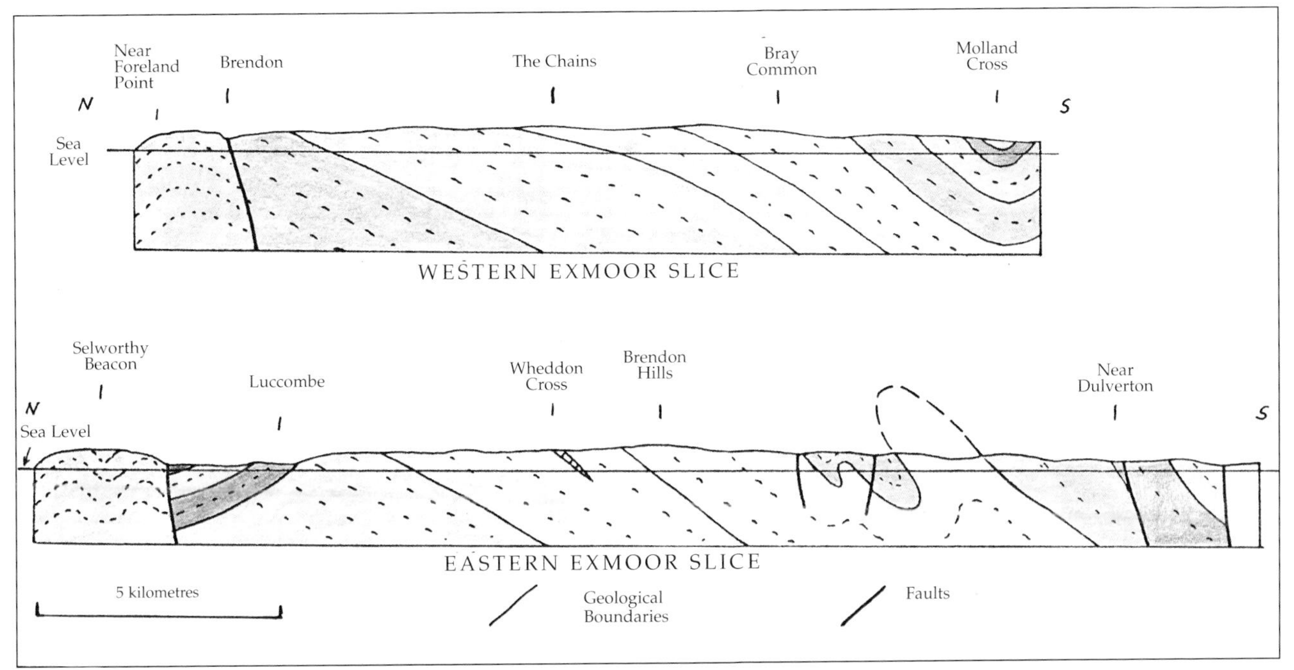

Plate 5. *Red Triassic sandstones in Holloway Street, Minehead.*

Photo courtesy of B.G.S.

Plate 6. *'Head' in the cliffs at Porlock Beach, near Porlock Weir.*

Plate 7. *The 'Punchbowl' near Winsford Hill – a possible glacial corrie?*

a hollow on the side of a hill or mountain gouged out at the head of a **glacier**.

Another smaller feature which may have been partly shaped by ice is Raven's Nest [SS 7777 4095], a north-facing hollow and cleft on the south side of the valley of the River Exe about one and a quarter miles north of Simonsbath which you can reach from the car park [SS 768 410] at Prayway Head.

During the greatest extent of the last ice sheet, about 18, 000 years ago, vast amounts of water were locked up in the ice and sea level fell all over the world by at least 100m. As a result, most of what is now the Bristol Channel north of Exmoor became land, through which flowed the ancestor of the River Severn. When the last ice sheet began to melt, about 10,000 years ago, sea level began to rise, rapidly between 10,000 and about 5000 years ago, and much less rapidly from then until the present. As the sea rose, woods around the coasts were drowned. Remnants of these '**submerged forests**' are present all round the shores of the Bristol Channel, and they have been found in Porlock Bay and offshore from Minehead.

During the rapid rise in sea level, a shingle beach made up of pebbles of Devonian sandstone formed, and moved towards the land as the sea rose. This beach now forms an impressive shingle ridge which extends across Porlock Bay between Hurlstone and Gore points (Plate 8).

At the eastern end of the ridge, the pebbles are smaller and rounder than at the western end, suggesting that they are being moved by waves and currents from west to east. You can also see similar shingle ridges at other places along the coast of the National Park, for example at Embelle Wood east of Glenthorne, and at Greenaleigh near Minehead.

Deposits which are being laid down along the flat bottoms of river valleys at the present day are called **alluvium**, which is mainly made up gravel and loam. Only the larger rivers such as the Barle and Exe have these flat **flood-plains** underlain by alluvium. **River terraces**, mainly made up of gravel, are the remains of old alluvium that has been left at levels above the present river flood-plains. They can mainly be found on the eastern side of the National Park between Porlock and Allerford, in Porlock Vale. Also in Porlock Vale there are extensive spreads of river gravel brought down Horner Water and Hawkcombe Water.

The main areas of **peat** on Exmoor are in the Simonsbath area, for example on The Chains and on Exe Plain. Peat on The Chains is nearly 10ft (3m) thick in places. The peat mostly began forming about 3000 years BC. Before the peat began to form, it seems that woods of oak, with hazel, birch, pine, alder, elm and lime, grew on Exmoor.

Plate 8. *Porlock Bay from Bossington Hill, showing the shingle ridge and the flooded area behind it (October 1996).*

Chapter 3

THE SHAPE OF EXMOOR

Exmoor is a high tableland which has been cut into by wooded valleys. On the north the plateau descends to the sea by a series of **hog's-back** cliffs (Plate 9). The present surface of Exmoor shows three main ridges which trend roughly E-W or ESE, and thus follow the geological 'grain' of the underlying Devonian rocks. The northern ridge runs inland from Foreland Point along Culbone Hill. The main central ridge extends from The Chains in the west to Dunkery Hill in the east. The southern ridge runs from Shoulsbarrow in the west to East Anstey Common in the east. These features represent the remnants of an extensive plateau which has been cut into by the main rivers and their tributaries.

The most obvious features of the Exmoor landscape today, ignoring the changes made by man, are:

– the **coastal cliffs**, at present being shaped by the erosional action of the sea.

– the **coastal plains**, largely shaped by deposition after the melting of the last ice sheets.

– the **upland plateaux** of inland Exmoor, which probably originated as a land surface about 25 million years ago.

– the **rivers and valleys** cut into the plateau surface

COASTAL CLIFFS

The coastline of the National Park between Combe Martin and Minehead is – with the notable exception of Porlock Bay – almost continuously made up of cliffs of the **hog's-back** type. A walk along any part of the coastal path is a delight, with constantly changing vistas. These cliffs are made up mainly of Hangman Sandstone, except for the stretch from Lynmouth Bay through Lynmouth to Woody Bay and Heddon's Mouth which is made up of **Lynton Formation**, and the area around Combe Martin which is made up of **Ilfracombe Slates**. Arber, in his classic book on the coast scenery of North Devon, distinguished two types of cliff profile: flat-topped cliffs and **hog's-back cliffs**. Such cliffs are characteristic of most of the coastline between Combe Martin and Minehead. As compared to flat-topped cliffs which have a near-vertical face with a flat or very gently seaward-sloping top, hog's-back cliffs show a long steep seaward slope above a rather small seacliff at the base of the slope (Plate 9).

An interesting feature of parts of the coast is the presence of **coastal waterfalls**. Those on hog's-back cliffs are not as spectacular as those developed on flat-topped cliffs (such as in the Hartland district), but some are quite fine. The best examples are those at

Photo courtesy of B.G.S.

Plate 9. *A view of Little Hangman (far distance) and Lester Point (mid-distance), Combe Martin, taken in 1932, showing the hog's-back shape of the cliffs. The landslip near Lester Point has now gone, revealing an old trial adit (Plate 15).*

Woody Bay (Plate 10), at Hollowbrook and at the mouth of Sherrycombe. The falls owe their origin to active erosion by the sea which has cut into the lower parts of hanging valleys.

I have given more detailed descriptions of the coastline from east to west, with descriptions of features of particular physical or geological interest, in the Places To Go section of the book (page 43 onwards).

Plate 10. *The coastal waterfall at Woody Bay.*

COASTAL PLAINS

The Hangman Sandstone cliffs are interrupted between Hurlstone Point and Gore Point by the broad 2-mile wide sweep of Porlock Bay (Plate 8). The bay owes its existence to the presence of underlying less resistant red Triassic mudstones which extend along the Vale of Porlock to link with similar submarine outcrops of mudstone. One of the most impressive gravel beaches in England extends across the bay between Hurlstone and Gore points.

A '**submarine forest**' is present in Porlock Bay on the seaward side of the shingle ridge, but it is not normally visible except at very low tides. Old accounts describe tree trunks of alder and oak over 20ft (6 m) long. The trees were rooted into **head** and surrounded by blue mud. The forest and its associated beds are between about 7800 and 5000 years old and show that there was a steady rise in sea-level over this period. This rise was the result of the melting of the last ice sheets.

Behind the shingle ridge lies an area of marsh deposits called Porlock Marsh which (with the ridge itself) is a Site of Special Scientific Interest. Recent breaching of the shingle ridge has led to flooding, especially in 1981 and 1990 (when 250 acres of farmland were flooded). More recently, I visited Exmoor on 29 October 1996 after the gales of the day before, and found the marshes extensively flooded (Plate 8). The ridge has been breached, and the breach has continued to widen, allowing regular flooding at high tides. Debate has centred on various options. One possibility, following a current trend in general coastal management policy, is to allow the wetland behind the ridge to flood naturally, and revert to **saltmarsh** or some form of lagoon, depending on how the ridge responds. Another option, now discarded, was to attempt to keep the ridge intact by moving shingle from less vulnerable areas, in order to protect the farmland behind.

On the landward side of the marsh are extensive areas of gently sloping river gravels between Porlock and Bossington.

East of Minehead, but mainly outside the National Park, is another coastal plain underlain by Triassic mudstones and sandstones and covered by **saltmarsh deposits, river gravels, head** and some wind-blown sand.

UPLAND PLATEAUX

If you drive or walk across Exmoor, your general impression will be of a high plateau with a roughly flat surface, which has been quite deeply cut into by

Plate 11. *A general view of west Exmoor and The Chains, looking west (from grid reference SS 762 436), showing the high plateau surface of Exmoor.*

Plate 12. *A dip-and-scarp feature in the Hangman Sandstone at Trentishoe Down.*

the main rivers and their tributaries (Plate 11). Although the plateau seems to have 'planed off' the underlying geology, there are still places on the Devonian rocks where the geology seems to be related to topographical features. For example, east of Combe Martin you can see a clear feature (Plate 12) in the Hangman Sandstone which can be followed from Little Hangman through Great Hangman, Holdstone Down, Trentishoe Down, Heale Down and South Down to the Parracombe area, and is probably due to harder layers in the sandstones.

Probably the clearest connection between the underlying geology and topography is shown in the eastern part of the National Park, in the Vale of Porlock and around Minehead. There, the younger Triassic red rocks are less resistant to erosion than the Devonian sandstones, and so form lowland areas surrounded by hills of the more resistant Devonian rocks.

RIVERS AND VALLEYS

A 'drainage divide' runs roughly east-west across the northern part of Exmoor and separates rivers and streams flowing north to the Bristol Channel from those that flow south and mostly (via the River Exe) into the English Channel.

The streams that flow north have short steep courses and include The River Umber at Combe Martin, the River Haddeo entering the sea at Heddon's Mouth, the West and East Lyn rivers reaching the sea at Lynmouth, Hawkcombe Water flowing to the sea near Porlock, and Horner Water meeting the sea near Bossington. The River Avill flows through Dunster to the sea east of Minehead. Horner Water has an interesting entry to the sea. Its course is blocked by the shingle ridge that extends across Porlock Bay (see page 47), and normally it filters through it to join the sea. At times of flood and high tide, however, it is said to burst through the ridge sending hundreds of tons of pebbles into the sea.

South of the drainage divide, the gradients are gentler and the rivers longer. The main rivers draining this part of the moor are the River Exe and its tributary the Barle. The source of the Barle is at Pinkworthy Pond, while the Exe has its source about 2 miles away at Exe Head near Simonsbath. Another tributary of the Exe, the River Haddeo, drains the southern flanks of the Brendon Hills. It has been dammed to form Wimbleball Lake.

A fairly small part of the western and south-western part of the National Park is drained by the rivers Bray, Mole and Yeo.

Some parts of the valleys of the various rivers are affected by the underlying geology and structure of the rocks. For example, some valleys follow faults, like the River Umber which runs along the NW-SE fault valley along which Combe Martin has developed.

An interesting feature of some Exmoor valleys is the presence of **valley-floor knolls** – distinctive ridges and knolls of rock which occur along the floors of some valleys. There are good examples along the Barle, Exe and Oare Water valleys (Plates 13 and 49). They probably represent areas of slightly more resistant rock separated from the valley sides by faults or joints which have been selectively eroded by stream action, possibly when much more water was flowing down them.

The great Exmoor Storm of 15 August 1952 had a considerable effect on valley slopes by landslipping and gullying during heavy rain.

HOW DID THE EXMOOR PLATEAU FORM AND HOW OLD IS IT?

As in other walks of life, geology has its fashions, and in the 1950s and '60s the fashion in understanding landscape was to try to recognise flat '**erosion surfaces**' at various heights above sea level. Some of these were thought to be the remains of **wave-cut** platforms cut by the sea many millions of years ago. It seems more likely that the bluffs on Exmoor, which are supposed to be the old cliffs at the back of the wave-cut platforms, are **dip-and-scarp** features or other surface expressions of the solid geology.

Professor Straw (see Further Reading section on page 93) has recently emphasised that, rather than the many 'flats' and 'surfaces' identified by earlier authors, *the* impressive feature of Exmoor is that there is *one* upland plain that cuts across all rock types. This plateau has a gentle slope from north-west to south-east, and a height range of about 490ft (150m) over a large area. In the east, the Brendon Hills reach over 1300ft (400m) above OD; at Dunkery Hill the height is 1700ft (519m); in Exmoor Forest over 1300ft (400m).

Plate 13. *Valley-floor knolls in the valley of the River Exe near Warren Farm, Simonsbath.*

WHY DOES EXMOOR FORM HIGH GROUND?

One of the most intriguing puzzles of Exmoor is why it stands higher than the surrounding country, especially compared to the area west of the National Park where identical Devonian rocks occur but have not given rise to high moorland. The question has recently been considered by Professor Straw, who has provided a fascinating insight into the reason why Exmoor stands as an upland above the surrounding country. The surface at this level was contrasted with a lower surface at about 900ft (275 m) OD west of a line between Combe Martin and Molland and also in central Devon. Straw considered that these were the same surface, a **subaerial** land surface of **Oligocene** age. He concluded that central and east Exmoor represent a fault-bounded massif which was raised by 490-650ft (150-200 m) above the adjacent country in mid-Tertiary times (about 25 million years ago).

Chapter 4

TREASURE FROM THE GROUND

Mining for Iron, Silver, Lead and Copper on Exmoor

Although it cannot rival the great Cornish mining industry in number of mines and output, Exmoor has a long and fascinating history of mineral working. The metalliferous deposits have been dug over a long period, traditionally since Roman times. A piece of iron slag 'from the Dulverton area' in the Bristol Museum contains Roman coins, and Romano-British pottery of the second century BC from Sherracombe is apparently associated with iron slag. The name 'Roman Lode' has been applied to workings near Raleigh's Cross in the Brendon Hills, and there is a 'Roman Lode' at Deerpark Mine near Simonsbath.

If you look at the map (Figure 2) on page 18, you will see that the mines of Exmoor fall roughly into the following four groups:

- **silver-lead and iron mines of Combe Martin**
- **iron mines of the Simonsbath area**
- **iron mines of the Brendon Hills and Eisen Hill**
- **iron and copper-iron mines of the North Molton area**

The most important deposits worked were the **iron ores** in the Brendon Hills and the **silver-lead** ores around Combe Martin. Near North Molton, some iron ores also contained useful amounts of copper, worked for example at Bampfylde Mine. All the ores I have mentioned so far are found in the **Devonian** rocks, but on the eastern side of the National Park, iron ore has been dug from **Triassic breccias**, at Luccombe (Knowle Top or Wychanger Mine) and at Brockwell, near Wootton Courtenay.

We will briefly tour these main mining areas and mention some of the main mines. It would be impossible to describe all the mines thoroughly in this book, but if you are interested in more information about the mines and mining history, there are several detailed accounts which I have listed in the Further Reading section. All the mines of Exmoor are now long disused.

SILVER-LEAD AND IRON MINES OF COMBE MARTIN

There has been mining around Combe Martin on and off from the late thirteenth century to the end of the nineteenth century. The earliest mines were sunk for silver, and the earliest date of working that we know of was in the reign of Edward I in 1293, when 337 Derbyshire men were moved south to work them. The last major time of working was in the reign of Elizabeth I. There have been various attempts to reopen the workings since then, without much success. The nineteenth century operations were mainly just trials.

Interesting details of the industry and mines are given in the book *Exmoor's Industrial Archaeology* (see Further Reading, p.93).

The earliest workings probably run more or less along the present main street of Combe Martin, close to the line of the **fault** that runs along the valley. Most of the old workings are now obscured, but you can see some remains of old mines at Knap Down Mine [SS 5975 4667] (Plate 14) and Combe Martin Mine [SS 5889 4654]. A walk to these mines is described in the Places to Go section of the book (page 69). You can also see traces of mineralisation at Lester Point in Combe Martin Bay (page 68). In the cliff near Lester Point you

Plate 14. *The ruined engine house of Knap Down Silver Mine, Combe Martin.*

Plate 15. *A trial adit for silver near Lester Point, Combe Martin.*

can see old adit which was uncovered in 1984 when storms washed away the rubble covering it (Plate 15).

The mineralisation is found in the **Ilfracombe Slates**. The main **ore** mineral is **galena**, a heavy silvery-grey lead mineral. Other minerals include the iron mineral **siderite, sphalerite** (a shiny black zinc mineral) and minor amounts of **chalcopyrite** and **pyrite**. Some mineral specimens may be spotted in the surface of Corner Lane in Combe Martin, which has been surfaced with mine spoil (see the Silver Mines Walk on page 69).

There are also some iron mines north-east of Combe Martin, in the upper part of the Hangman Sandstone. The walk described on page 69 includes a visit to old workings near Blackstone Point, some in precarious situations on the cliff top. Because of the great difficulties of working in these out of the way situations, these mines had only a short life in the last century. The ore was dropped to the shore and then loaded onto small sailing ships which took it to the South Wales ironworks.

IRON MINES OF THE SIMONSBATH AREA

Iron mining on Exmoor is thought to have begun between the second and fourth centuries BC. The earliest form of extraction was to dig the ore out from trenches. An example of these early works can be seen near Cornham Ford (see Places to Go, p. 75).

Around Simonsbath, you can find the remains of a number of old iron mines, mainly within the **Morte Slates**, and extending between Cornham Ford and Blue Gate. The westernmost mine is Deerpark Mine and the workings east of Blue Gate are called Exmoor Mine. You can find details of a walk to Cornham Ford on page 75.

Wheal Eliza ('Uncle Ben's Gold Mine' of the book *Lorna Doone*), on the banks of the River Barle south of Simonsbath, differs from the other mines in this area in that it was opened for copper as well as iron. It was worked between 1846 and 1854. The mine is in the **Ilfracombe Slates**, close to the boundary with the **Morte Slates**. The ore is mainly **siderite** with some **chalcopyrite** and **pyrite**. A walk which includes a visit to the sparse remains of mining activity at Wheal Eliza is described on page 73. Nearby small iron mines were worked at Picked Stones in the **Morte Slates** and Honeymead in the **Ilfracombe Slates**.

FREDERIC KNIGHT AND THE IRON MINES OF EXMOOR FOREST

Frederic Knight of Simonsbath was closely involved with the attempt to develop the iron mines of Exmoor Forest, mainly between 1850 and 1860. Unfortunately, none of the mines ever came up to expectation, and it is said that by 1858 the company concerned (the Dowlais Iron Company) had spent £6000 to mine £950 worth of ore.

THE RAILWAY TO PORLOCK WEIR THAT NEVER WAS

During this saga, it was soon recognised that it was vital to get any ore that was produced to the markets, and as a result it was proposed to build a railway to the coast at Porlock Weir. The route chosen was Prayway Head-Warren Farm-Tom's Hill-Larkbarrow-Hawkcombe Head-Whitestones (just above the Porlock-Lynmouth road). The line was planned to reach Porlock Weir by two inclines. But the railway was never built, owing to lack of capital. Several sections were, however, actually surveyed and cut in 1856-7, and you can still recognise them on the ground. You can see traces on Porlock Common (for example, at SS 846 461, easily reached from the car park at Pittcombe Head [SS 841 463]) and at Elsworthy, extending nearly to Warren Farm northeast of Simonsbath.

Various other schemes for railways or aerial ropeways were proposed at various times, and details are given by Roger Burton in his book on Exmoor Forest (see Further Reading, p.93). Most fascinating of these was an aerial ropeway from Cornham Ford to Porlock Weir, proposed in 1910, which proved to be too expensive to build.

There was a renewed interest in working the iron mines in 1909-1914, but they proved to be just as financially unsuccessful as the mid-nineteenth century attempts.

IRON MINES OF THE BRENDON HILLS AND EISEN HILL

If you look at the map showing the mines of Exmoor (Figure 2), you will see that there is a line of old iron mines extending more or less east-west for about 9 miles between Eisen Hill [SS 908 371] (also spelt Ison or Eyeson) in the west to Yeanon [ST 059 334] in the east. There are many mines in this belt, including Kennisham Hill, Gupworthy, Burrow Farm, Bearland Wood and Raleigh's Cross. The area is riddled with old **shafts** and **adits**, and 81 had been counted up to the year 1985. The deepest mine was Raleigh's Cross at 820 ft (250 m). A plan of the underground workings of Raleigh's Cross Mine and the nearby Carnarvon Mine is shown in Figure 4.

The **ores** occur with **quartz** in **veins** up to 25 ft (7.6

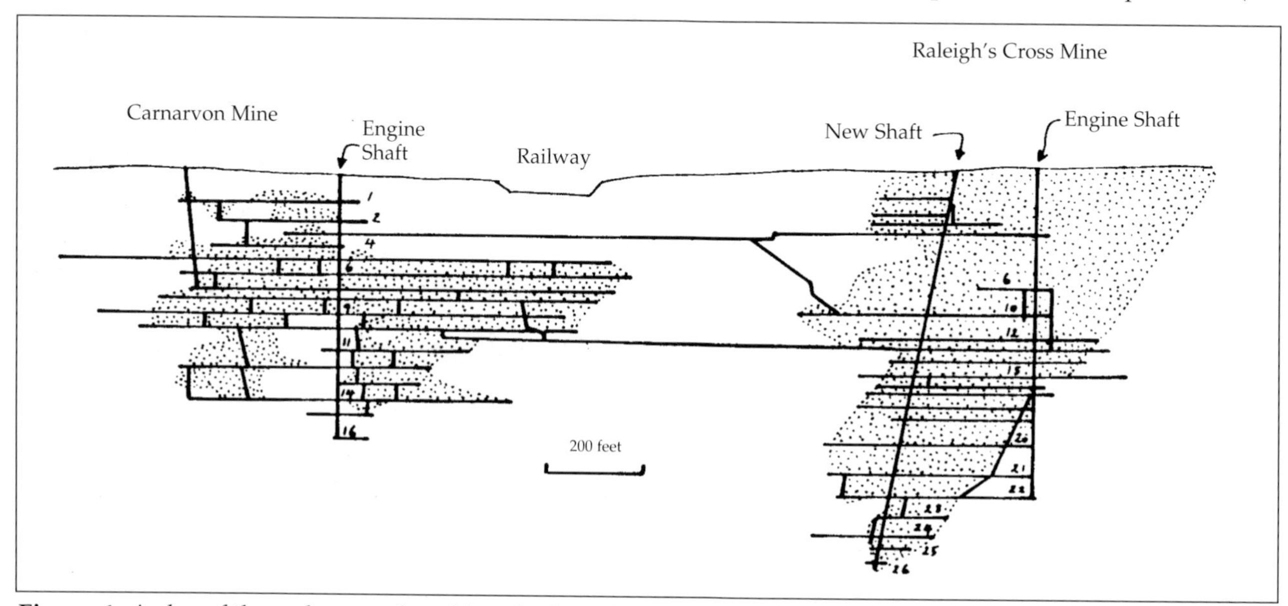

Figure 4. *A plan of the underground workings in the Raleigh's Cross and Carnarvon mines at Brendon Hill.*

m) wide which are tilted steeply to the south, sometimes following **bedding** planes and sometimes **cleavage**. The ores occurred in lenticular pockets. The main ore mineral was **siderite** (iron carbonate), also known as '**spathic ore**'. Other iron minerals, such as **hematite, limonite** and **goethite** probably resulted by oxidation of the siderite nearer to the surface. Manganese also occurs, and traces of copper minerals have also been found.

The iron of the Brendon Hills has probably been worked since ancient times, but production by modern methods began in about 1850, when several of the mines were worked by the Ebbw Vale Company. It is difficult to believe if you visit the area now, but the isolated villages of Brendon Hill and Gupworthy were once thriving communities with houses, church and chapels, schools and shops. However, everything depended on the mines and once they closed, the villages faded away almost overnight. Mining ended in the 1880s, although there was a failed attempt in 1908-1914 by the Somerset Minerals Syndicate to revive the industry. The total recorded amount of ore dug from the Brendon Hills and Eisen Hill between 1855 and 1909 was 765,553 tons, and the peak production of 46,894 tons was recorded in 1877. The years of prosperity ended in 1875, but the mines were worked for four more years until sudden closure with a week's notice in 1879. However, with a brief revival in trade, some of the mines soon reopened, and continued production until 1883 when competition from Spanish ore became too great. The last three mines (Kennisham Hill, Burrow Farm and Colton) stopped work in September 1883. These closures were more gradual and caused less distress to the miners than in 1879. There was a brief re-opening in 1907-10 and then the mines closed for good.

THE WEST SOMERSET MINERAL RAILWAY

The iron ore was transported from the Brendon Hills to the port of Watchet along the West Somerset Mineral Railway for shipment to the blast furnaces of South Wales. The railway extended from Gupworthy in the west to Brendon Hill, a distance of about 4 miles. From there, the ore was transported down from the top of the Brendons by a half-mile-long 1 in 4 incline to Comberow and from there a further 6 miles through Roadwater and Washford to Watchet for shipment. Surviving photographs show that the Great Incline, opened in 1858, was an impressive sight during its working period (see Plate 16) but regrettably it has become overgrown and fallen into ruin, and there is currently no public access to this monument to Victorian engineering. The winding house at the top of the incline (shown in the photograph, Plate

Photo H.H. Hole

Plate 16. *An old photograph (1897) showing the Great Incline of the West Somerset Mineral Railway between Brendon Hill and Comberow. At the foot of the incline is the engine 'Pontypool' with passenger train.*

17, as it is today) was partly rebuilt in the 1930s, but is now ruined and in dangerous condition; the rest of the incline is overgrown and privately owned. The winding house contained two drums 18 ft (5.5 m) across which shared an axle. By using steel cables, the weight of iron ore in trucks going down the incline could be used to raise empty trucks.

Plate 17. *The ruins of the winding house at the top of the Great Incline, Brendon Hill.*

The West Somerset Mineral Railway was legally obliged to remain open even after the mines which were its main reason for existence had closed, and it continued to carry passengers until its closure in 1898. On the Great Incline, the old winding method could not be used after the mines had closed, and instead a small stationary engine was installed in the winding house. By this means, passengers could travel up the incline in a truck, without payment but at their own risk!

During the First World War, the rails were commandeered for scrap by the Ministry of Munitions, and by 1919, the line was left without rails or rolling stock. The land was finally sold by auction in August 1924 bringing to an end the story of this fascinating little line.

The full story of the West Somerset Mineral Railway and an account of the Brendon Hills iron mines is told in the book by Roger Sellick. Other information about iron mining on Exmoor can be found in the book *Exmoor's Industrial Archaeology* (see Further Reading).

After the mines closed, the mine buildings soon decayed. In the case of the Brendon Hills, the machinery was removed, the shafts sealed and the buildings fell into ruin. The Raleigh's Cross Mine buildings were blown up in 1907 for ballast for working the Great Incline, and buildings at Gupworthy and Kennisham Hill were demolished for building stone. There are very few surface structures now left; of the last two engine houses remaining in the Brendon Hills area, the one at Kennisham Hill [SS 963 362] has been demolished, but fortunately that at Burrow Farm has been partly restored and is well worth a visit (see Places To Go, page 81). It stands next to part of a cutting of the West Somerset Mineral Railway.

IRON AND COPPER-IRON MINES AROUND NORTH MOLTON. GOLD.

A few iron ore veins around North Molton contained sufficient copper to support mining, particularly at Bampfylde (or Poltimore Mine) [SS 738 327], Molland [SS 819 283] and Gourt [SS 823 282] mines. The mines are within the **Pickwell Down Sandstone**, and the veins are east-west, dipping steeply north and south. New Florence Mine [SS 750 320], near Tabor Hill, produced 39,000 tons of sideritic ('**spathic**') and hematitic ore between 1873 and 1885.

The ores were transported from Bampfylde and New Florence mines by narrow gauge tramway to connect with the main line east of South Molton station; the banking is still visible in fields below Marsh Farm.

Bampfylde Mine (also known as Poltimore Mine), near Heasley Mill, is the largest and best known working in the area. It was active early in the eighteenth century and abandoned and revived at various times. The dumps of mine waste along the eastern bank of the River Mole show how extensively this area was worked.

Traces of gold have been found at a couple of localities at Bampfylde. In a scandal in the 1850s, samples of ore were 'salted' with gold dust to produce favourable test results and raise the share value.

An account of mining activity with details of individual mine sites and the remains visible today can be found in the book *Exmoor's Industrial Archaeology* (see Further Reading, p. 93).

IRON MINES OF THE TRIASSIC BRECCIAS

Not all the iron mines are found in the Devonian rocks, and some of the Triassic **breccias** in the east of the National Park have been affected by iron mineralisation, for example at Luccombe and near Brockwell, Wootton Courtenay (see Places To Go, page 51). The mineralisation at Luccombe appears to have occurred by replacement and cementation of breccia. **Hematite** is the main ore mineral. The two mines (at Luccombe and at Brockwell) were apparently worked together, and the iron ore was shipped to South Wales from Porlock and Minehead. The mines were producing in 1837, but had stopped by 1858. They reopened for a short time in 1870.

HOW DID THE EXMOOR ORES FORM?

Geologists have long puzzled over how the Exmoor ores formed. In Cornwall and around Dartmoor, there is an obvious connection between the tin and copper mineralisation and the presence of the granites which occur along the spine of the South West England peninsula. In the case of the Exmoor ores, the distance from the Dartmoor Granite seems to rule out an obvious connection. Instead, some geologists have suggested that fluids moving at fairly low temperatures through the Devonian rocks leached from them low concentrations of metals which were then deposited in fractures, resulting in the localised and irregular pockets of ore which are typical of Exmoor.

Chapter 5
USEFUL STONE

All over Exmoor we find scattered small old quarries and pits from which a whole range of useful materials were dug in the past, whether for building stone, roadstone, brick clay, gravel, or for limestone to burn in kilns to make lime.

STONE FOR BUILDING

Over much of Exmoor, local **Devonian** stone was dug from small pits and quarries to use in buildings and roads. There are some bigger quarries, such as the one below Conygar Tower near Dunster, which was probably a roadstone quarry. The quarry at Hollerday Hill, near Lynton, was worked for building stone for the town, from sandstone beds in the **Lynton Formation**.

Even if some of the local stone was not of the best quality, people preferred to use it because it was so expensive to bring in better stone from farther away. Rubbly surface slate and sandstone provided much of the material for dry stone walls, of which there are many on the moor. You can see good examples near Simonsbath, and one is shown in Plate 18.

The Devonian stone is difficult to trim into regular shapes, and it has generally been used in ragwork or rubble fashion. Ancient churches (for example, at Culbone), have rubble towers, but some (for example, at Watchet) have towers of massive ashlar blocks. Devonian sandstones (**Hangman Sandstone**) has been used in the construction of the church at Oare (Plate 19), famous in fiction as the place where Lorna Doone was shot on her wedding day.

The farm buildings constructed by the Knight family during their reclamation of Exmoor Forest (1881-1898) were built of local Devonian slate and sandstone,

Plate 18. *A dry stone wall made of local slate near Simonsbath.*

Plate 19. *Devonian sandstone used in the tower of Oare Church.*

Plate 20. *A wall of Triassic sandstone in Minehead.*

although the lack of good roofing slate on Exmoor meant that Welsh slate had to be shipped in through Lynmouth. You can see typical examples of Knight farmsteads at Pinkworthy, Driver, Duredon, Cornham, Emmett's Grange and Wintershead.

On the eastern side of the National Park, various stones have been quarried from the **Triassic** rocks around Porlock and Minehead. The stone is usually not as hard as the Devonian stone, but can be trimmed to regular shapes more easily. The main sources of Triassic building stone were the better-cemented sandstones, especially those from Staunton Quarry at Alcombe, south of Minehead. The warm pale reddish

Plate 21. *St Michael's Church, Minehead, showing the use of Blue Lias limestone (grey) and Triassic sandstone (red).*

Plate 22. *Minehead Hospital, showing the use of imported golden brown Jurassic limestone and red Triassic sandstone.*

brown (sometimes greyish green) sandstone from there has been widely used in buildings and walls in Minehead town (Plate 20). There were probably also sandstone quarries in the town, for example, one near St Michael's Church, Higher Town.

The lower part of the red mudstones (**Mercia Mudstone**) in the Vale of Porlock contains some sandstone beds, and these have been dug in a few places for building stone. For example, sandstone from Burrowhayes Quarry at West Luccombe was used for buildings in Porlock and Minehead in the 1930s, but I understand that it was found to be too porous to use in houses.

The '**Blue Lias**' limestones (**Jurassic**) from around Selworthy have been used in a small way for buildings. In Minehead, the tower of St Michael's Church, Higher Town, is mainly of grey **Blue Lias limestone** with some red **Triassic sandstone** (Plate 21).

Some imported **Jurassic** stones, such as **Ham Hill Stone** from near Yeovil, have been used in buildings in Minehead in combination with red **Triassic sandstone**, for example in Minehead Hospital (Plate 22).

The **head** deposits which are common over Exmoor (see page 16) were an easy source of rubbly sandstone and slate which could be used to build field walls and farm buildings.

SLATE

Most of the **slate** of Exmoor is not particularly suitable for roofing slate, although it has been used as such,

Plate 23. *The restored limekiln at Woody Bay.*

Photo courtesy of B.G.S.

Plate 24. *Large fold in the Hangman Sandstone at Culver Cliff, Minehead.*

Plate 25. *Small folds at Culver Cliff, Minehead, formed by 'slumping' of sand down a shallow slope during Devonian times.*

and for facing houses exposed to the weather. Some better slate can be found in places, and the best known workings in the National Park were around Treborough [ST 015 367], north of the Brendon Hills, where the Ilfracombe Slate was worked at various times from the 1400s until the quarries closed in 1938. There is a record of the quarry supplying 2000 slates to Dunster Castle in 1426 for 20 old pence. It produced roofing slate and slate slabs for flagstones, doorsteps etc.

The quarries were started on outcrops of slate on the hillside, but as the workings became deeper, drainage tunnels were dug to get rid of water from the quarries.

The old quarry [ST 015 367] was south of the road between Treborough and Roadwater, and is now filled in. Newer quarries on the west side of the road were started in 1863. There were apparently some underground workings beneath this quarry. The slate was hauled from the old quarry through a tunnel to the mill. The quarry was about 300 ft (91 m) deep by the end of the century, and water was then pumped out mechanically. The large amounts of waste typical of slate quarrying produced the large tips that can be seen today (it is said that for every ton of slate produced there may be up to 20 tons of waste). There was a bed of cleaved, crystalline, fossiliferous **limestone** about 6ft (2 m) thick in the quarry, and it was also apparently intersected in the (locked) tunnel that runs beneath the road. It may be equivalent to a limestone bed at Roadwater where it is about 26ft (8 m) thick. Limestone was also worked at Treborough in quarries [ST 019 368] east of the Old Quarry. For those interested in more details of the West Somerset slate industry, there is an article by Chris Tilley in the Exmoor Review for 1993, and an account in *Exmoor's Industrial Archaeology* (see Further Reading, p. 93).

BRICKS AND TILES

As far as I can judge, the only formation in the National Park used for making bricks and tiles were the red **mudstones** (**Mercia Mudstone**) of the Porlock and Minehead areas. I have no definite evidence of brickpits from Porlock Vale, but near Minehead there was a large brickpit at Alcombe [SS 972 453]. The kilns, now demolished, were on the north side of the main road, and the clay was taken over the road by aerial ropeway. The workings, called the 'Victoria Brick and Tile Works' were started in 1897.

LIME

Limestone for burning to produce **lime** for spreading on fields to 'sweeten' the soil was generally brought in by boat from South Wales to the coast of Exmoor, and burnt in kilns which you can find scattered all along the coast. You can see a restored example at Woody Bay (Plate 23).

As well as the imported limestone, limestone from the Devonian rocks of Exmoor was worked for lime. The main source of local limestone was the **Ilfracombe Slates**, which contain discontinuous beds of limestone, especially around Combe Martin and between Exford, Wheddon Cross, Luxborough and Roadwater. The limestone at Combe Martin was burnt in kilns; there were eighteen kilns in the town at one time, and much of the lime was taken by horse and cart for use during the reclamation of Exmoor Forest by the Knight family. There were also quarries all along the line of the limestone beds farther east. At Newland Quarry [SS 824 385], about one and a quarter miles west of Exford, a complex of kilns, inclines, lime store cart shed and smithy served two quarries, the larger of which was worked until 1914.

There were at one time two water wheels at Newland Quarry. One was on Pennycombe Water. The other was some distance from the quarry, and was supplied by a leat flowing in a deep culvert along part of its length. The wheel was 25 ft (7.6 m) across and was partly underground, the tail water being returned to Pennycombe Water through a rock-cut tunnel. The pump was in a 70-ft (21 m) deep shaft near the larger quarry, and was worked by flat rods from the wheel, with another tunnel to take away the waste water. I have not checked these details myself, but have taken them from N. V. Allen's book on *The Waters of Exmoor* (see Further Reading, page 93).

For those of you interested in industrial archaeology, there is a description of the quarry by D. W. Warren (see Further Reading section).

The **Triassic** rocks in the east of the National Park were also dug for lime. At Alcombe Quarry, near Minehead, the quarrymen picked out pebbles of limestone from the Triassic **conglomerate** and burnt them in kilns on the spot. At Gillhams Quarry [SS 9197 4445], near Luccombe, they worked a thick **vein** of **calcite**, probably for lime, although I have not been able to find a kiln.

There are small pits on the red **Triassic** mudstones west of Minehead, between Wydon Farm and Woodcombe, and these were probably dug to get **marl** (limy clay) to spread on fields.

Chapter 6

PLACES TO GO AND THINGS TO SEE

In this part of the book, I will guide you to places where you can best explore the rocks and scenery of Exmoor. We shall concentrate first on the coast, following it from Minehead in the east to Combe Martin in the west, since this is where the geology is best seen and where most people go. Then I shall pick out some inland places of interest.

A WORD ABOUT SAFETY

Safety is mainly commonsense, but parts of Exmoor could be dangerous if you don't take some simple precautions. These include:

– make sure you have the right sort of boots and clothes for the weather.

– always check the state of the tides. There is a big tidal range in the Bristol Channel and tides come in quickly. Make sure you always have an escape route.

– don't go close to cliff faces which may be unstable. Don't try to go up or down cliffs by unrecognised paths.

– be very careful on rocky foreshores which often have slippery boulders.

– although the moors may not be as remote and wild as some in Britain, some parts (for example The Chains) are quite high and remote and should be avoided in bad weather (especially when it is misty) unless you know how to use a compass.

– don't go into or too near old mine shafts and adits – they can be very dangerous.

MINEHEAD

Minehead does not have any obvious connection with mining, and its name probably comes from the Welsh word *mynydd*, meaning hill, after the prominent hill that dominates the town. The red **mudstones** and **sandstones** of **Triassic** age which underlie much of Minehead are less resistant than the surrounding hills of **Devonian sandstone**, so the town occupies a hollow in the hills. The built-up area of the town has also spread out eastwards onto the coastal flats of **saltmarsh deposits** and **river gravels**.

A GEOLOGICAL TOWN WALK IN MINEHEAD

This walk is a pleasant ramble from the centre of Minehead up to the oldest and highest part of the town. During it you can look at building stones, see some of the Triassic sandstones and get fine views over the town towards Dunkery. It is best to choose a clear day to get the best of the views.

You can conveniently start from Minehead Station, terminus of the West Somerset Railway, where there is a large car park. Just east of the car park is Butlin's 'Somerwest World' holiday camp which is built on quarry hardcore dumped on the **saltmarsh** deposits in 1961-62.

Walk towards the centre of the town into The Avenue, along which examples of different building stones can be seen. At the junction of North Road and The Avenue, large split cobbles of **Hangman Sandstone**, probably from beach shingle, have been used in buildings. The commonest type of building stone is warm pale reddish brown or greyish green **Triassic sandstone**, obtained from old quarries in the town or from Alcombe Quarry south of the town. You can see typical examples in walls in North Road, where some blocks show honeycomb weathering. Along The Avenue, local stone has in places been used with imported stone. In the Hospital, for example, squared blocks of **Triassic sandstone** have been used with golden brown **Ham Hill Stone (Jurassic)** imported from the Yeovil area (Plate 22). Some carved blocks of this stone have been used in the NatWest Bank building next to Market House Lane.

From the western end of The Parade, turn off northwards up Holloway Street, where you can see some red **Triassic sandstones** (Plate 5) and **breccias** [SS 9674 4638] inclined fairly gently northwards. The sandstones show **cross-bedding**, and what you now see are probably fossil sand dunes. Farther north, just below the junction with Clanville Road, you can see fine-grained **breccias** with some small **faults**.

Continue up The Ball to reach St Michael's Church in the attractive Higher Town part of Minehead. In the base of the wall below the church, a small patch of red **sandstone** shows that the church is built on the **Triassic sandstones**. However, the steep rise behind the church marks the **Hangman Sandstone**, and there is a big fault between the Triassic sandstones and the Devonian sandstones.

Stop in front of the church and take in the view over Minehead and south and east of the town. The town occupies a valley filled with red **Triassic sandstones** and **mudstones** which have been let down like a trapdoor against the big **fault** behind the church. The mudstones were worked for bricks in a pit which you may be able to make out near the Fire Station at Alcombe. The hills south of Minehead, such as Conygar with its distinctive tower, are formed of Devonian Hangman Sandstone. In the distance on a good day, you will be able to see Dunkery Beacon, the highest point on Exmoor and made up of **Hangman Sandstone**.

The flat ground to the east, around Somerwest World, is formed mainly of clayey saltmarsh deposits, with a belt of sand dunes north of the camp. In front of these is a shingle ridge which extends eastwards to Blue Anchor.

The church itself is built of a variety of interesting stones, among which are buff and reddish brown **Triassic sandstone, Blue Lias limestone** (Lower Jurassic), and buff limestones which are possibly Middle Jurassic. The tower is mainly of **Blue Lias limestone** and **Triassic sandstone** (Plate 21).

From the church, you could return to Minehead Station via Church Path and The Esplanade, or, depending on how energetic you are feeling, you could carry on walking (via Beacon Road and the zig-zag path down to the Harbour) to link with the following walks to Culver Cliff and/or Greenaleigh.

CULVER CLIFF AND GREENALEIGH

You can take a short walk to Culver Cliff to look at the **Hangman Sandstone** and examples of **folds**. An optional extension for the energetic can be made to Greenaleigh to see the **shingle ridge, head, Hangman Sandstone**, and a good example of an **anticlinal fold**. *You need a low tide for these excursions.*

Begin the Culver Cliff walk at the car park at Quay West, Minehead. From there, walk westwards along a path which goes along the edge of a flat grassed area formed of tipped material, with a shingle ridge on the seaward side. Groynes have been constructed along the ridge to slow down erosion of the ridge and protect the vulnerable tipped ground behind from erosion. At the western end of the grassed area, stay at beach level and continue for about another 300 yds (274 m) until Culver Cliff is seen.

The cliffs are up to about 90 ft (27 m) high and are made of **Hangman Sandstone**. The **sandstones** are stained red in places, and there are also some **mudstones**. If you stand back and look at the cliff you will see that the sandstone layers have been bent into a large **fold** (Plate 24). The layers on one side have been tipped up on their side so that they are nearly vertical, while the layers on the other side are fairly flat-lying. It is an example of the buckling which affected the Hangman Sandstone during the mountain-building movements about 300 million years ago. You can also see cracks in the rocks (**faults**), especially where the two sides of the fold come together and the strain was greatest.

Some sandstone beds contain pieces of mudstone which were ripped up from soft layers of mud when the sandstones were formed. A few pebbles of **quartz** occur in some sandstones. At beach level, you can see a distinctive 9 ft (2.7 m)-thick bed of grey sandstone which shows folds (see Plate 25). They are different from the normal sorts of folds which are caused by pressure during earth movements. Instead, they probably formed by slumping of the sandstones down a shallow slope when they were laid down.

You can continue this walk to Greenaleigh if you wish by retracing your steps to the western end of the grassed area referred to above, and from there taking the steep path westwards to join Greenaleigh Lower Road which you then follow to Greenaleigh Farm (about half a mile). From near the farm you will get good views of the coastal features, which consist of an apron of **head** (under farmland) in front of which is a very small area of **saltmarsh deposits** and a well developed curved shingle ridge. Take the public footpath across the fields to the western end of the **shingle ridge**. There, you will see that the head has been cut into by the sea and can be seen in cliffs up to about 18 ft (5.5 m) high. It consists of orange-brown sandy gravel with fragments of Hangman Sandstone. These head deposits probably formed during a cold period of the **Ice Age** by freezing and thawing which caused movement of waterlogged soil and other material in a porridge-like fashion down slopes.

West of the head cliffs, the cliffs of **Hangman Sandstone** begin, and in the most easterly of these you can see unstable tall columns of **sandstone** defined by

joints (cracks in the rock along which there has been no movement). Nearby, you can see the sandstones folded into an excellent example of an **anticline**, with joints cutting across it (see Plate 2).

When you have finished, you need to retrace your steps to get back to your starting point at the Quay West car park.

NORTH HILL, SELWORTHY BEACON AND BOSSINGTON HILL

Between Minehead and Hurlstone Point, North Hill and Bossington Hill form a block of **Hangman Sandstone** which is separated by big faults from the **Triassic** rocks to the south. The ridge rises to a height of 1010 ft above sea level at Selworthy Beacon. A road extends from Higher Town, Minehead, along North Hill to a car park near Selworthy Beacon; this is a popular drive, since you get superb views of Porlock Bay from its western end, and Bossington Hill is within easy reach.

You will see excellent views of the coastal features around Porlock Bay by looking west from Bossington Hill [SS 901 485] (Plate 8), and I have described these features in the section on Porlock Weir and Porlock Bay (below, page 51).

If you are driving or walking along the road from North Hill to Selworthy Beacon and are interested in **mineralisation** you might be interested to stop off at Combeshead Quarry [SS 9283 4767], about half a mile east of Selworthy Beacon. There, in the central part of the north face of the quarry, you can see a brecciated vein up to 8 inches wide cemented by the minerals barite and hematite. **Barite** is recognisable by its distinctive heavy weight, and **hematite** is a dark iron mineral. Please do not hammer the vein, or take samples, but leave it for others to look at.

THE COAST FROM GREENALEIGH TO HURLSTONE POINT

The coastline west of Greenaleigh as far as Hurlstone Point is isolated and difficult to get at. Some deep combes, such as East Combe and Henners Combe, do cut down into the cliffs, but they all involve a scramble down to the beach, and I would not recommend trying these routes.

The cliffs are made of **Hangman Sandstone**, with the layers generally inclined to the north. Most of the coastal slope along this stretch shows old **landslips** which extend inland for up to a quarter of a mile, for example, at Western Brockholes [SS 918 491] where you can see some quite impressive slipped masses of shattered sandstone forming blocks and ridges separated by areas of angular boulder **scree**. At other places, the old landslipped areas can be recognised by uneven hummocky ground. You can get to the Western Brockholes by using the 'Rugged Coast Path' created by the National Trust, which skirts the top of the cliffs between North Hill and Porlock Bay. Details of this and others paths on the National Trust's Holnicote Estate are given in a leaflet ('Explore Holnicote') produced by the Trust. However, I would not recommend scrambling around amongst the landslipped areas!

BOSSINGTON AND HURLSTONE POINT

Hurlstone Point is an interesting place to look at **folds** and **faults** in the Hangman Sandstone and to see the eastern end of the **shingle ridge** across Porlock Bay. You can reach it easily from Bossington, where there is car park. *You will need to go at low tide if you want to see the west-facing part of the headland.*

From the car park at Bossington, cross the footbridge and turn left towards Hurlstone. After about 0.6 mile, you should take the steep footpath down to the obvious headland of Hurlstone Point. At the base of the cliff, you will find yourself at the eastern end of the impressive **shingle ridge** that crosses Porlock Bay. At this end of the ridge the pebbles, which are all of **Devonian sandstone**, are smaller and rounder than at the western (Gore Point) end. This suggests that the pebbles are being moved from west to east.

Plate 26. *A syncline in the Hangman Sandstone at Hurlstone Point.*

Hurlstone Point is a good place to see the **Hangman Sandstone** and the **folds** and **faults** that affect it. At the northern end of the shingle ridge, the sandstones are folded into a **syncline** (see Plate 26).

In the small headland [SS 8985 4918] west of the fold, you can see sandstones which were mostly laid down in river channels (Plate 27). Some of the sandstone beds show well-developed **convolute lamination** (see Plate 28). This type of structure was probably formed by the liquefaction of soft sandstone.

You can get at the west-facing part of Hurlstone

Photo courtesy of B.G.S.

Plate 27. *Ancient (Devonian) river channel sandstones in the Hangman Sandstone at Hurlstone Point.*

Photo courtesy of B.G.S

Plate 28. *'Convolute lamination' in Hangman Sandstone at Heddon's Mouth, formed by liquefaction of soft sand.*

Point with great care at low tides, but keep a close watch on the state of the tide and be careful on the rocks. This is for the agile only! You can see the layering (**bedding**) in the sandstones inclined to the north. You may also see small **folds**. Some obvious cracks (**faults**) fractures cut across the headland (Plate 29). A small cave, worn out by the sea along a fault, cuts through the headland.

From Hurlstone Point you have various choices for different return routes to the car park at Bossington. One possibility is for you to walk up Hurlstone Combe (a steep pull, but worth it for the views from the top). You can see good examples of **scree** close at hand along the north side of the combe (Plate 30). This material consists of angular sandstone rubble weathered from solid rock probably mainly by frost shattering.

Photo courtesy of B.G.S

Plate 29. *Faults cutting through the headland of Hangman Sandstone at Hurlstone Point.*

Photo courtesy of Mr H. C. Prudden.

Plate 30. *Scree covering the valley side in Hurlstone Combe.*

From the top of the combe, continue towards Selworthy Beacon along the coast path, but before reaching it, turn right and descend by either Lynch Combe or Holnicote Combe and return to the car park at Bossington via Allerford. Alternatively, you could continue over Selworthy Beacon and then down Selworthy Combe to Selworthy (see below) and then back to Bossington via Allerford. A look at the

Ordnance Survey 1:25 000 Outdoor Leisure map will make these routes clearer.

SELWORTHY

The picturesque and much-visited village of Selworthy is sited at the northern boundary of the only occurrence of **Jurassic** rocks in the National Park. These belong to the part of the Lower Jurassic called the '**Blue Lias**', which you can best see along the Somerset coast from Blue Anchor eastwards. The Blue Lias is also well known from Lyme Regis in south Devon, where collectors have found the remains of giant sea reptiles like *Plesiosaur* (please-ee-oh-saw), as well as many **ammonites**. The Blue Lias is made up of grey **mudstones** with regular layers of thin **limestone**.

Photo courtesy of Mr H. C. Prudden.

Plate 31. *'Knoll' scenery in Luccombe Breccia country.*

The word 'Lias' is thought to have arisen from quarrymens' corruption of the word 'layers'. Large east-west **faults** running just south of Selworthy Church have let down the Blue Lias against the **Devonian sandstones**.

The church forms an excellent viewpoint, and from it you can see Dunkery Beacon in the distance to the south, weather permitting. The lower ground in front of you, between Selworthy and Dunkery, is the Vale of Porlock, a hollow filled with red **Triassic breccias** and **mudstones** which pass up into the Blue Lias rocks nearer Selworthy. The woods just below Selworthy, between Buddle Hill and East Lynch Farm, conceal old pits in the Blue Lias. The wooded ridge, which you can see along the north side of the A39 road, is also formed of the '**Rhaetic**' beds, **black shales** and **limestones**, which pass down into grey and then red Triassic mudstones.

AROUND LUCCOMBE

Luccombe is a picturesque village near the southern edge of the Vale of Porlock. It is located in **breccia** country which gives rise to characteristic scenery of small steep-sided hills 'knolls' (Plate 31). The 'knowle' of place-names such as Tivington Knowle and Wootton Knowle is probably derived from the word 'knoll'. This knoll type of country contrasts with the flatter ground to the north, around Holnicote and Blackford, which is underlain by red mudstones.

You can see examples of the **breccias** and an unusual '**Boulder Bed**' in Huish Ball Steep, north of the village. From the small car park [SS 912 446] in the village, walk north and take the second lane (Huish Ball Steep) on the right, past East Luccombe Farm. In about 300 yds (274 m), you will see the 'Boulder Bed' nicely displayed in the sides of the lane (Plate 4). The bed is about 15 ft (4.6 m) thick and is made up of quite well rounded boulders of purple **Devonian sandstone**. It was probably deposited in the channel of an ancient river.

Underneath the Boulder Bed you can see finer-grained **breccias** more typical of the Luccombe area. They consist of angular pieces of **sandstone, slate** and **quartz**. These breccias were laid down on **fans** of debris derived from what were then mountains to the south, possibly around 250 million years ago.

Also near Luccombe, at Wychanger or Knowle Top Mine, there are old workings (probably opened in 1820) for iron on the hill top [SS 913 445]. The **mineralisation** appears to have occurred by replacement and cementation of **breccia**. A wood has now grown over the old workings, which consist of two trenches trending WNW-ESE. Dump material around the eastern end of the northern open working shows intense replacement of **breccia** by hard purple-red **hematite** cementing **quartz** pebbles. There is not a great deal to see now, and you can visit the old workings only by permission of the landowner at East Luccombe Farm.

You can find similar, but more extensive, surface workings at Brockwell [SS 928 429], near Wootton Courtenay.

PORLOCK WEIR AND PORLOCK BAY

Porlock Weir is an attractive small harbour, mainly used by leisure boats, kept open by dredging the channel through the **shingle ridge**. It is a good place from which to view and explore the coastal features of Porlock Bay, especially the shingle ridge. You can get good views of Hurlstone Point, which you can reach by following the coast path along the shingle ridge (but, following the October 1996 breach, only at low tide).

Between **Hurlstone Point** and **Gore Point**, the cliffs of Hangman Sandstone are interrupted by the broad sweep of Porlock Bay, about two miles wide. The bay owes its existence to the underlying less resistant red **Triassic mudstones** which extend along the Vale of Porlock to link with similar mudstones beneath the bay. You will also see one of the most spectacular shingle beaches left in England extending across the bay (Plate 8). The ridge and the area of marsh behind called Porlock Marsh are a Site of Special Scientific Interest.

WHAT TO DO ABOUT THE SHINGLE RIDGE?

Because it has become starved of pebbles over the last 200 years, the sea has at times broken through the shingle ridge, flooding the land behind. The most recent flood was in October 1996 (Plate 8). There has been much discussion on what to do. A recent trend in 'coastal management' is to work with rather than against coastal processes. This means that, depending on the situation, a managed retreat approach might be taken. In this case, any breaches in the ridge would not be repaired and the marsh behind would be allowed to flood. This would, of course, affect the farmland behind the ridge. However, it is possible that mud might accumulate and eventually build up the level of the land behind the ridge. This approach would be much cheaper than trying to preserve the ridge.

A 'SUBMARINE FOREST'

There is a '**submarine forest**' in Porlock Bay on the seaward side of the shingle ridge, but it cannot normally be seen except at low tides. Old accounts describe tree trunks of alder and oak over 20 ft (6m) long. The trees were rooted into **head** and surrounded by blue mud. The forest and its associated beds are between about 7 800 and 5000 years old and show that the level of the sea rose steadily over this period. This rise was the result of the melting of the last **ice sheets** (see page 16).

HEAD AT PORLOCK WEIR

From Porlock Weir through West Porlock to Porlock, the farmland is underlain by **head** spreading out from the foot of the steeper Hangman Sandstone slopes to the south. The head consists of gravel with angular pieces of Devonian sandstone. Near Porlock Weir, low cliffs [SS 8690 4762] have cut into these head deposits, shown in Plate 6, and you can see them clearly by taking a short walk eastwards from the car park at Porlock Weir.

WEST OF PORLOCK WEIR VIA GLENTHORNE TO FORELAND POINT

From Porlock Weir westwards to Glenthorne and Foreland Point, the cliffs are of **Hangman Sandstone** except at Embelle Wood where there is small length of **shingle ridge** with **head** behind it. The sandstones are mainly tilted to the north. Unlike the coast between Minehead and Hurlstone Point, the coastal slope is covered by woods as far as Glenthorne. This is the longest stretch of coastal woodland in England; sessile oaks are the commonest trees. The coastal path has been partly diverted by **landslips** (see below) but you can use it to get to the much visited Culbone Church which makes a pleasant walk from Porlock Weir. The church is built of rubbly blocks of the local **Devonian sandstone**.

There is no good way in to the base of the cliffs along this long stretch of wild and lonely coastline between Porlock Weir and Glenthorne. With the permission of the farmer, you can walk in from Broomstreet Farm [SS 817 485] down a zig-zag track through Embelle Wood to Embelle Wood Beach, but it is a long steep haul. It does give you the chance to see the 'Sun Stone' [SS 8222 4860] which has some inscribed verses on it.

Just west of Porlock Weir, the cliffs have recently been affected by active **landslips** (Plate 32), cutting the coastal path which has had to be rerouted. These and older landslips extend all the way along the coast to beyond Glenthorne.

Photo courtesy of B.G.S.

Plate 32. *Recent landslips in the cliffs just west of Porlock Weir.*

WHAT CAUSED THE NEW LANDSLIPS WEST OF PORLOCK WEIR?

The recent **landslips** may have been partly caused by waves and tides washing away previously slipped debris from the foot of the steep coastal slope. Landslipping is therefore more likely to happen during especially high tides, and during very uncommon storm-tidal surges, which may happen only every 10-100 years. It is significant that only one such surge happened in the century between 1880 and 1980, while two surges have already happened in the last decade. The earlier of these two tidal surges can be linked quite well with beginning of the recent slipping of the cliffs in the early 1980s.

A WALK FROM PORLOCK WEIR TO FIRST ROCKS

At *low tides*, you can take a short walk along the coastline westwards from Porlock Weir to look at the **shingle ridge, Hangman Sandstone** at First Rocks, an old **limekiln**, and the recent **landslips** which I have mentioned above. From the car park at Porlock Weir, walk westwards past the Anchor Hotel and continue past some converted old limekilns. Follow a track which roughly follows the boundary between **saltmarsh** on the north and a sloping head-covered slope backed by steep slopes to the south. After a few hundred yards, you will reach the **shingle ridge** which you should follow westwards. If you have been to Hurlstone Point, you can compare the pebbles there with the ones at this western end of the ridge. You will find the pebbles here larger and not so round as the ones at Hurlstone Point. This supports the idea that the pebbles are being moved from west to east.

At the western limit of the shingle, low cliffs of Hangman Sandstone begin and show **sandstones dipping** regularly to the east. At the eastern edge of the area of modern **landslip**, you will see a disused **limekiln** [SS 8554 4837]. If you continue on to First Rocks [SS 852 485], you can see sandstones showing layers of reddish brown **mudstones** with cracks caused by drying out of the mud soon after its formation.

If you like the wildness of this sort of coastline, the tides are right and you are not alone, you could continue the walk westwards to Culbone Rocks [SS 8442 4862] and Ivy Stone [SS 8387 4876]. At the Ivy Stone you can see conspicuous slabs of **sandstone** dipping steeply towards the sea. The Ivy Stone cannot be rounded at most states of the tide.

GLENTHORNE

You can walk down to the shore at Glenthorne by permitted paths from County Gate or Black Gate on the A39 road. There is an Exmoor National Park visitor centre at County Gate which is well worth visiting.

A Site of Special Scientific Interest for the Hangman Sandstone extends along the shore at Glenthorne from [SS 794 499], near Giant's Rib, to [SS 805 495], near The Caves. You need to *check the tides* if you are planning to walk along the shore.

Where Coscombe Water reaches the sea near Glenthorne, a small **coastal waterfall** (see page 22) is developed. Although this one is not particularly impressive, it is first of several to be found from here on westwards, and which I will mention in the appropriate place.

If you walk eastwards from Glenthorne to Glenthorne Beach and The Caves, you will see cliffs up to about 65 ft (20 m) high in red-stained sandstones with good examples of **folds**. At The Caves [SS 8031

Plate 33. *The Caves, near Glenthorne – vertical layers of sandstone with caves worn out along softer beds of shale.*

4947], you can see several narrow caves excavated along softer beds of **shale** within vertical **sandstones** (Plate 33).

If you go along the shore westwards from Glenthorne, you come to Giant's Rib [SS 7948 4990], where **sandstones** and **siltstones** form prominent slabs inclined towards the sea (Plate 34). There is a rock arch through the headland.

From Giant's Rib to Foreland Point, the shore is again difficult to get at safely. The cliffs are all in **Hangman Sandstone**. Another **coastal waterfall**, finer than the one at Glenthorne but not easy to reach, is present at Desolation Point, where Wingate Water reaches the coast. It is best seen from the sea.

Plate 34. *The Giant's Rib – slabs of Hangman Sandstone on the lonely coast west of Glenthorne.*

FORELAND POINT

Foreland Point [SS 755 512], formed of **Hangman Sandstone**, is one of the most prominent features of the National Park coastline. The reasons for the prominence of the headland are not immediately obvious, since it is composed of Hangman Sandstone much the same as elsewhere along the coast. It seems to owe its existence simply to the fact that it is where a ridge of Hangman Sandstone meets the sea. There are no obvious large faults that might have some effect on the form of the Point.

The centre line of the big **anticline** affecting the Devonian rocks (see page 11) meets the coast at Blackhead, just west of Foreland Point. North of this line the rocks are generally tilted northwards; south of it, they are generally tilted to the south.

A WALK FROM COUNTISBURY TO FORELAND POINT

From the National Trust car park at Countisbury, go north to follow the path on the western slopes of Butter Hill. There are steep drops to the left down to Sillery Sands. Soon you come to a major fenced-off cleft in the coastal slope called Great Red, where there is evidence of **landslips**. This slipping may be related to the presence of a **fault** which runs up Great Red. There are excellent views westwards over Lynton and Lynmouth. If you happen to be on this walk at a time of low tide, you will notice the distinctive, roughly triangular, gravel beach (Plate 35) at the mouth of the East Lyn river – more of this later.

There are various options now. The Ordnance Survey 1:25 000-scale Outdoor Leisure map will help you to plan your route. You could continue on to visit the lighthouse at Foreland Point – the northernmost tip of Devon – and then return along Coddow Combe on the east side of the Foreland. This is an impressive feature with steep scree-covered sides. The stream along the combe probably used to fall to sea over a cliff about 100 ft (30 m) high, but the water is now diverted to tanks to supply the lighthouse.

LYNMOUTH AND LYNTON

The attractive coastal resorts of Lynmouth and Lynton developed mainly in response to the Victorian enthusiasm for landscape tourism. Lynmouth is close to sea level at the meeting place of the East and West Lyn rivers, while Lynton is perched on a shelf about 480 ft (146 m) above Lynmouth. The well known cliff railway, opened in 1890, connects the two places. Lynton used to be connected to Barnstaple by narrow-gauge railway, opened in 1898 but closed in 1935.

LYNMOUTH TO WATERSMEET

The beautiful walk from Lynmouth along the valley of the East Lyn River to its junction with Hoaroak Water at Watersmeet is one of the best known walks on Exmoor and is described in many guidebooks. An interesting booklet in the 'Thematic Trails' series called *Lyn in Flood*, by Peter Keene and Derek Elsom, describes the landscape aspects of this walk, and also the Lynmouth Flood of 1952 (see page 61, below). If you drive along the road east from Lynmouth along the side of the East Lyn valley (Lyn Cleave and Myrtlebury Cleave), you will see many cuttings in the Lynton Formation.

LYNMOUTH TO SILLERY SANDS

If you walk eastwards along the shore from Lynmouth

Plate 35. *The gravel 'delta' at the mouth of the East Lyn River at Lynmouth.*

Plate 36. *A view of Foreland Point and Sillery Sands, looking north-east from near the A39 road about halfway between Countisbury and Lynmouth. The cliffs are made up of Hangman Sandstone.*

(*making sure the tides are right*), you can see typical rocks and structures of the **Lynton Formation**. The rocks consist of strongly **cleaved slates** with silty **sandstone** and clayey **siltstone** and are quite strongly affected by **folds** and **faults**. They are disturbed by **burrowing** in places and you may be able to spot some bands which may be full of **crinoid** (sea-lily) fragments. The **trace-fossil** *Chondrites* (described on page 12) is common. You may be able to see some fossil shells in loose blocks of sandstone between Perilous Point and Sillery Sands. A view looking northeastwards from near the A39 road about half-way between Countisbury and Lynmouth shows (Plate 36) Foreland Point with Sillery Sands in the foreground. The cliffs are made up of hard green s**andstone**, commonly red stained and with **quartz veins** near small **faults**.

Photo courtesy of B.G.S.

Plate 37. *The famous Valley of Rocks, Lynton. At the far end of the valley is Castle Rock, and on the right hand side are crags of Lynton Formation with screes spreading down into the head-filled valley.*

Plate 38. *'Rugged Jack', Valley of Rocks, Lynton – a 'tor' of Lynton Formation.*

Plate 39. *A view westwards along the coast from Castle Rock, Valley of Rocks, Lynton. The headland in the centre is Duty Point (with Duty Point Tower on the cliff top). Beyond are Lee Bay, Woody Bay and Wringapeak.*

THE LYNMOUTH-EAST LYN FAULT AT NINNEY WELL BAY

About 0.6 mile east of Lynmouth, there is a gully in the cliff at Ninney Well Bay [SS 735 495] which marks a big **fault** separating **Hangman Sandstone** on the east side from **Lynton Formation** on the west side. You can see from the geological map (page 18) that the fault then runs inland, partly along the East Lyn River, to Malmsmead.

From this fault, the Lynton Formation forms the coast as far west as Heddon's Mouth. In contrast to the Hangman Sandstone coast, there are several inlets, especially that of Lynmouth and also at Wringcliff Bay, Lee Bay and Woody Bay. The coastal slopes between Lee Bay and Woody Bay are heavily wooded, as also are the deeply cut valleys of the East and West Lyn rivers.

THE LYNMOUTH FLOOD OF 1952

At low tide, you will notice the distinctive, roughly triangular, gravel beach at the mouth of the East Lyn river (Plate 35). This **delta** is made up partly of a huge volume of debris brought down the East and West Lyn rivers during times of flood and dropped at the mouth of the river, and partly of debris derived from the nearby sea-cliffs by the action of the sea. One of the most recent major floods affecting Lynmouth occurred in 1952 and had disastrous effects. The flood resulted from exceptionally heavy rainfall on 15 August 1952, when large areas of the higher parts of Exmoor received over 8 inches of rainfall in 24 hours. The extensive catchment area of the two Lyn rivers received over 3 billion gallons of water. This huge volume of water and the transported material (including boulders of up to 50 tonnes) caused devastation in Lynmouth. The delta at the mouth of the river was formed during this and earlier floods, such as those of 1607 and 1769.

A fascinating guide to the East Lyn valley and the Lynmouth Flood is given in the 'Thematic Trails' booklet called *Lyn in Flood*, by Peter Keene and Derek Elsom.

THE VALLEY OF ROCKS

One of the most notable and much visited features of this part of the coast is the Valley of Rocks, a dry valley, now filled with **head**, which runs parallel to the coast between Lynton and Lee Bay (Plate 37). You can get to it by driving and parking in one of the car parks in the valley, or a more pleasant and scenic approach is to walk from Lynton along North Walk on the north side of Hollerday Hill. At the eastern end of the North Walk you will obtain excellent views eastwards to Foreland Point, then, as you carry on walking westwards, views of the coast to the west open up.

The rocks that you can see in the valley are **sandstones** and **slates** of the **Lynton Formation** that extend from the west side of Crock Point through Lee Bay and the Valley of Rocks and beyond. The sandstones have been quarried for building stone at Hollerday Hill, near Lynton.

There is a large car park on the valley floor, with an interesting display board describing the origin of the valley.

If you stand in the valley and look north (towards the sea) you will see a line of prominent rocky crags, which include 'Rugged Jack' (Plate 38) and, at the western end of the valley, Castle Rock. They are made up of **sandstones** and some **slates**, and are divided up into blocks by cracks (**joints**). They are inclined fairly gently to the east and south-east.

Beneath the crags on the north side of the valley, you can see screes – angular chunks of sandstone – which merge downslope into the head deposits which fill the valley floor. In Wringcliff Bay (see below) the head deposits are at least 200 ft (60 m) thick.

If you look across to the south side of the valley, you will see that there are no screes, the slopes being mainly covered with bracken. However, there are five rock ridges that appear to have been cut off at their ends. Some people have suggested that this might have been done by ice moving down the valley during the last **glaciation**. On one of the ridges you can see the fancifully named 'Devil's Cheesewring'.

Castle Rock forms an obvious feature at the western end of the valley and most reasonably fit people can climb it without too much difficulty. You can obtain excellent views of the coast westwards from the top of Castle Rock (Plate 39). You are quite likely to see some of the wild goats that live on the crags and scree of the valley. Beside the path near the base of the rock, you can see crags showing good examples of **cleavage** and **bedding** (see Plate 40). The bedding is inclined at a shallow angle and is cut by the more steeply inclined cleavage.

Near the summit of Castle Rock, you may be able to locate some **ripple marks** on **bedding** surfaces, like the ones that you can sometimes see on a sandy beach. They were formed by the movement of sand by currents in shallow water. You can also see on the surface of the rock **slickensides** which are parallel scratches produced by movement of adjacent rock layers during folding or faulting (Plate 41).

Plate 40. *Lynton Formation at the foot of Castle Rock, Valley of Rocks, showing examples of cleavage and bedding.*

Plate 41. *Parallel scratches ('slickensides') in Lynton Formation at the top of Castle Rock, Valley of Rocks, produced by the movement of adjacent rock layers during folding or faulting.*

You may be able to find fossils at a few places in the Lynton Formation exposed in the Valley of Rocks. For example, at the base of the 'Devil's Cheesewring' you may be able to find a thin layer of pale **limestone** that contains broken stems of **crinoids** (sea-lilies).

HOW DID THE VALLEY OF ROCKS FORM?

The coastal erosion theory

It seems that the most likely explanation for the origin of the Valley of Rocks is that it used to be part of the Lyn valley at a time of low sea levels when the river reached the sea farther west than it does at present. As sea level rose, the sea cut into the side of the valley, so creating a new outlet at the present site of Lynmouth, and causing the Valley of Rocks to be abandoned as a dry valley. The East and West Lyn rivers then cut gorges down to the level of the new outlet, leaving the Valley of Rocks at a higher level.

One interpretation of the westward continuation of the former river valley from the Valley of Rocks is that it extended through Wringcliff Bay to Duty Point (where there is a coastal bench) and onwards to Crock Point. It was argued that the Valley of Rocks could not have continued over the higher rock col of Lee Abbey, and that the Lee stream once flowed eastwards to join the Valley of Rocks stream at Wringcliff Bay.

The ice sheet theory

Another theory of the origin of the Valley of Rocks suggests that an **ice sheet** pressed up against the coast of Exmoor, damming the mouth of the River Lyn

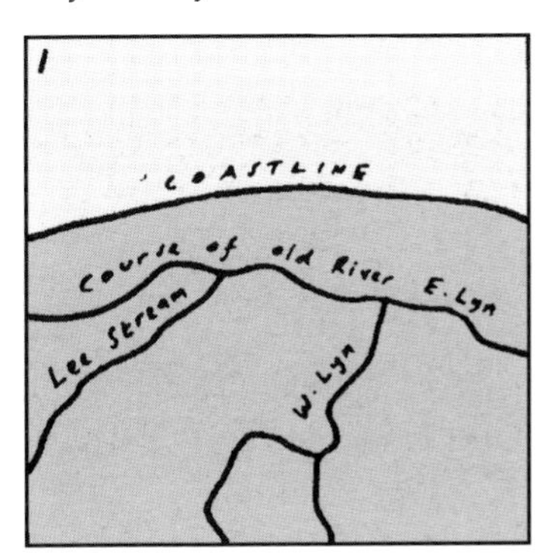

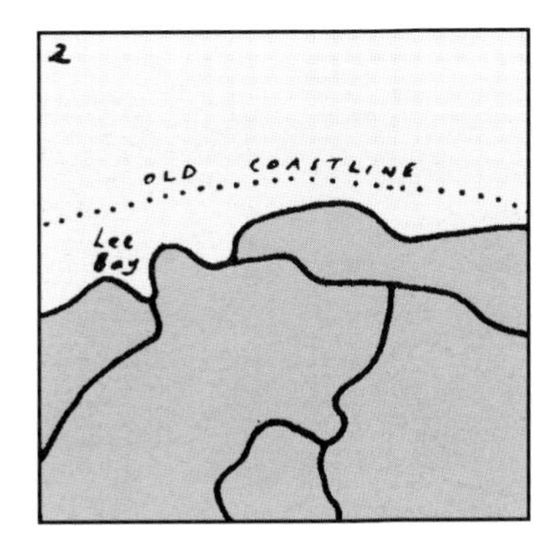

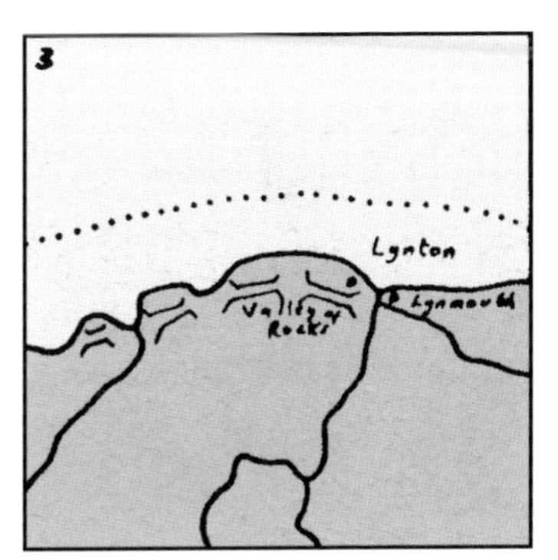

Figure 5. *Theories on the origin of the Valley of Rocks, Lynton.*

There are various opinions concerning the way in which the Valley of Rocks formed. One, shown here, suggests that it is an old valley of the River Lyn cut deeply when sea level was lower than at present. A rise in sea level caused the sea to break into the valley, giving a new outlet at Lynmouth and leaving the Valley of Rocks as a dry valley.

1. The old River Lyn flows westwards roughly parallel to the coastline.
2. Erosion by the sea causes the coastline to retreat southwards, cutting into the valley of the East Lyn, firstly at Lee Bay.
3. The present situation. Eventually the coastline breaks into the East Lyn at Lynmouth, giving the East Lyn and West Lyn a new outlet to the sea, and causing the Valley of Rocks to be abandoned as a dry valley.

(thought to be in more or less its present position) and resulting in the formation of a lake. The lake then overflowed to the west, carving a channel with a mouth farther west along the coast. When the ice melted, the River Lyn resumed its original course, leaving the Valley of the Rocks abandoned at a higher level.

After the river valley was left dry, it filled with thick deposits of **head** during a cold climate in the **Ice Age** when shattered rock debris and finer grained material flowed down the valley sides.

An interesting booklet on the Valley of Rocks in the 'Thematic Trails' series has been produced by Peter

Plate 42. *Typical Lynton Formation at Lee Bay.*

Keene and Brian Pearce and is well worth reading if you would like more detailed information on the valley.

The coastal erosion theories on the origin of the Valley of Rocks are summarised in Figure 5.

WRINGCLIFF BAY, LEE BAY, WOODY BAY AND HEDDON'S MOUTH

Wringcliff Bay and Lee Bay are cut into the western continuation of the Valley of Rocks, and in both bays you can find thick deposits of the **head** which fills the valley. You can reach Wringcliff Bay by going down a steep zig-zag path from near Castle Rock in the Valley of Rocks. In the main indentation of the bay, you can see that the head deposits go down to beach level and must be at least 200ft (60 m) thick. The fragments in the head get larger downwards and at beach level include small boulders, most of them angular but some well rounded.

You can reach Lee Bay easily from the nearby car park, and it is a good place to see the **Lynton Formation** (Plate 42). The formation here contains **sandstone** beds which can be traced from the west side of Crock Point through Lee Bay to the Valley of Rocks and beyond. The rocks are mostly dark green **sandstones** and **siltstones**, and some dark grey **slates**, with no obvious fossils. Some surfaces show **ripple marks**. You can see a fair amount of 'wispy' **bedding** and the beds have been churned up by burrowing organisms.

You can see the **head** deposits of the Lee Abbey valley at the back of Lee Bay. There, about 65 ft (20 m) of head rests on top of about 13 ft (4 m) of gravel with some small well rounded pebbles of **sandstone, slate** and **quartz**, together with some **flint**. You can find a detailed interpretation of the deposits, suggesting an upward sequence from a **raised beach** through an old river bed to **head** and finally soil, in the interesting 'Thematic Trails' guidebook to the Valley of the Rocks that I mentioned earlier.

CROCK POINT

The flat coastal platform of Crock Point is underlain by **head**. Clay was supposed to have been worked there at the end of the eighteenth century by Dutchmen. After the digging had finished there was a large **landslip** and it is said that the beach was covered with huge chunks of brightly coloured red, yellow, brown and white clay.

WOODY BAY

There is a car park [SS 676 486] above Woody Bay from which you can walk down the steep hairpin road to the shore. The return trip to the car park can be tiring. On the shore, you can see the remains of a pier, all that is left of a failed nineteenth century attempt to develop the bay into another tourist resort like Lynmouth. There is a restored **limekiln** on the beach (Plate 23).

In the bay you can see **Lynton Formation**, consisting of greenish grey slates and silty **slates**, which are sometimes stained red. There are some large boulders on the foreshore. The **dip** of the **beds** is generally to the south, and cleavage is well developed. You may be able to find some bedding surfaces in slaty rocks covered with branching tubes of sandstone. These structures, called *Chondrites*, are one of the most characteristic features of the Lynton Formation (Plate 43). Where *Chondrites* is very common, the term 'tunnel sandstone' has been used to describe the appearance

Plate 43. *Trace-fossils, probably including* Chondrites, *at Woody Bay.*

of the rock. *Chondrites* probably formed by the action of a worm which fed on the soft sediment by means of an extensible 'nose'.

The stream, Hanging Water, that flows down to Woody Bay ends in a **coastal waterfall** about 30 ft (9.1 m) high (Plate 10).

WOODY BAY TO HEDDON'S MOUTH

The **Lynton Formation** forms the lower part of the cliff from west of the pier in Woody Bay westwards through Wringapeak to Heddon's Mouth. Sandstones of the **Hangman Sandstone** occur in the higher part of the cliff. You can see the transition between the Lynton Formation and the Hangman Sandstone near Great Burland Rocks [SS 666 497] and also at Hollow Brook [SS 669 495]. You can get there from the car park above Woody Bay, by going west to the hair-pin bend and then following the coastal footpath to the cliff-top exposures. The Lynton Formation consists of grey **sandstones** and **mudstones** which become sandier upwards as the base of the Hangman Sandstone is approached. The lower part of the Hangman Sandstone consists almost entirely of sandstone, and may have formed on an ancient beach. Before reaching Great Burland Rocks you will cross Hollow Brook, which reaches the sea in what is said to be one of the highest and finest **coastal waterfalls** in North Devon, but can only be well seen by boat (trips are available from Lynmouth).

A CIRCULAR WALK TO HEDDON'S MOUTH

The walk from Hunter's Inn to Heddon's Mouth and back is a pleasant two mile round trip. There is a National Trust car park, shop and information centre at Hunter's Inn. From the car park go past the Inn and follow the stream along Heddon's Mouth Cleave, which here has a flat bottom occupied by **alluvium**. At the northern end of these alluvial flats, the valley sides become if anything even steeper and are covered in scree on both sides. The steep valley is cut in **Hangman Sandstone**, but as the beach is approached, **Lynton Formation** is seen at the beach. The transition to Hangman Sandstone occurs higher in the cliff.

FROM ELWILL BAY TO LITTLE HANGMAN

The **Lynton Formation** is last seen at Ramsey Beach, on the east side of Elwill Bay, and from there westwards to Little Hangman the cliffs consist of **Hangman Sandstone**. They are the highest cliffs in southern England and at Great Hangman rise to over 1000 ft (305 m) above sea level. This stretch of coast is not easily and safely accessible and the beach is very bouldery. The cliff scenery is very fine and can be seen from the coastal footpath; unlike the wooded stretch around Woody and Lee bays, the cliff tops are open

Photo courtesy of B.G.S.

Plate 44. *Folds at Wild Pear Beach, Combe Martin. See Figure 3 for an explanation of folds, bedding, and cleavage.*

and excellent views are possible. The hills just inland include Trentishoe Down (Plate 12), Holdstone Hill, Great Hangman and Little Hangman, all made of Hangman Sandstone.

There is a fine **coastal waterfall** at the mouth of Sherrycombe, with a fall of about 100 ft (30 m) on to the beach. Again, you can see this best from a boat (trips are available from Ilfracombe).

The western end of this stretch of coast is at Little Hangman (Plate 9). You can get some idea of its structure by viewing it from the west side of Combe Martin Bay, from where you can see that the headland consists mainly of south-dipping **Hangman Sandstone** faulted at Wild Pear Beach against the overlying **Ilfracombe Slates** which are **folded** into **anticlines** and **synclines** (Plate 44).

From the large **fault** at Wild Pear Beach, the **Ilfracombe Slates** form the coast to Combe Martin and then to Ilfracombe and beyond. The slates produce a different type of coastline, characterised by lower cliffs with cultivated summits. The coast is broken by small headlands separated by narrow coves.

COMBE MARTIN

Combe Martin, at the western boundary of the National Park, is the focus for a number of excursions to examine local places of geological, landscape and mining interest. You can find an informative display on the geology of the area at the Exmoor National Park Information Centre in Combe Martin.

The town is sited on the **Ilfracombe Slates**. These contain significant **beds** of **limestone**, which were worked in several quarries on the west side of the town. The limestone was burnt in **limekilns** which operated from the eighteenth to the early nineteenth century. **Umber**, a mineral pigment, was in the past worked from rotted limestones at Combe Martin. The main minerals of interest in the area were, however, silver, lead and iron. You can buy an inexpensive leaflet describing walks to local silver and iron mines at the Information Centre. I have described the mines of the area briefly in Chapter 4.

Combe Martin Bay may partly owe its formation to the presence of a major NW-SE trending **fault** forming a line of weakness exploited by the River Umber, along which the village, said to have the longest main street in England, has developed.

You will need *low tide* to explore the east side of Combe Martin Bay as far as Lester Point. On the east side of Combe Martin Beach, the **Ilfracombe Slates** are grey **slates** with some **beds** of **siltstone** and **sandstone**. You can see the **trace-fossil** *Chondrites* (page 12) on some surfaces (Plate 1), and the slates are **folded** in places. Just south of Lester Point, a mine adit about 100 ft (30 m) long was probably an unsuccessful nineteenth century trial for silver (Plate 15). **Quartz veins** (Plate 3) cut across the adit, but it is not likely that they carry significant minerals. The end of Lester Point is known as Camel's Head. In the rocks here you may be able to see traces of the lead mineral **galena** and the zinc mineral **sphalerite** along the **cleavage** of the slate. The mineral **lode** has been quarried and worked from a shaft which forms the eye of the 'camel'.

On the west side of the beach, you can see the grey to dark grey 'Combe Martin Beach Limestone' which contains **corals** and **bivalves**.

You cannot currently get to Wild Pear Beach because of a **landslip**, but I include some details of interesting localities for the time when it is again possible to get to the beach. On Wild Pear Beach, the **Ilfracombe Slates** lie between two NNW-SSE **faults**. The rocks are strongly **folded** and cleaved silvery grey **slates** with thin **sandstones, siltstones** and **limestones**. At the eastern end of the beach [SS 582 478], you can see where the big **fault** that extends inland to Parracombe reaches the coast. On its north side you can see fairly undisturbed **Hangman Sandstone**, but on the south side, the **Ilfracombe Slates** are squeezed by earth movements into tight **folds** (Plate 44). The Hangman Sandstone here is the youngest part of the formation showing a change from river to sea deposition, and you may be able to find a bed with fossil sea shells (*Myalina*).

At the foot of the path to Wild Pear Beach and at various places along the base of the cliff you can see places where pebbles and other material have been cemented by lime into a concrete-like substance known as **tufa**. The lime probably came from springs issuing from limestone beds within the slates.

OLD MINES AROUND COMBE MARTIN

Walks to see the sites of former mining activity are described in an inexpensive leaflet available from the Information Centre in Combe Martin, and I have based the following descriptions on the leaflet.

A Walk to Knap Down Silver Mine

The walk begins at the junction [SS 598 468] of Girt Lane and Vellacott Lane. You can park on the verges of both lanes. Go uphill along Vellacott Lane and take the next right. Turn right again at the next junction, into Corner Lane; you will soon see the chimney of Knap Down Mine **engine house** (Plate 14). The buildings are in dangerous condition and should not be entered. Workings and shafts of the mine, the last to work silver in the district, are present on both sides of the lane. The engine house, operating between 1843 and 1868, pumped water from a 138 ft (42 m) deep shaft.

Continue down the lane, passing Silver Mines Farm on the left; the lane below it is surfaced with mine spoil, and you may be able to find examples of the following minerals: **siderite** (iron); **sphalerite** (zinc); **cupropyrite** (copper); and **galena** (lead). The silver was generally contained in tiny amounts in the galena, and you cannot see it. Continue towards the bottom of Corner Lane; before its junction with Watery Lane, gorse-covered mounds on the left are the remains of Harris's Shaft, part of Old Combmartin Mine, closed in 1848. Four **lodes** of silver/lead **ore** were worked beneath the hillside and beneath the village. Follow the lane until Watery Lane joins on the right and follow it to turn left into Pentice Lane. This lane is typical of sunken lanes in the Combe Martin district, and cuts through **Ilfracombe Slates**. The slates weather and break up along the cleavage planes. You can see '**terminal curvature**', formed by down-slope movement under gravity of the upper layers of the slate, near the surface.

At the top of Pentice Lane turn right and walk a short way up Shute Lane before turning off left up Knap Down Lane. Although the lane is on slates, the walls are faced with red **Hangman Sandstone** with some white **quartz**. Turn right at the junction with the next lane (Girt Lane) and return to the start of the walk.

Iron Mines of Blackstone Point

There are a group of workings for iron in the Hangman Sandstone around Blackstone Point, north-east of Combe Martin. You can get to them either from Combe Martin, using the old miners' track around the north-east shoulder of Great Hangman, or from the same starting point [SS 598 468] as the silver mines walk described above. From there, walk up Girt Lane, eventually crossing the coast path, and continue to Blackstone View Point. The deep combe to the right is Sherrycombe, at the northern end of which is a **coastal waterfall**, visible from the sea. At the cliff edge, Great Hangman Gut drops dramatically to the sea. Above the track are trials for iron, and shortly after an old

adit. It is dangerous to continue past the sign. There are two further mine entrances beyond, the main entrance being perched precariously on the cliff edge. There are three further adits at shore level, and another at Little Hangman. You can retrace you steps to the start of the walk at Girt Lane, or you can make this into a longer walk by returning to the coast path and walking westwards along it over Great Hangman and Little Hangman to Combe Martin, and then return to your starting point via Rocky Lane and Knapp Down Lane.

INLAND EXMOOR

Now that we have completed our exploration of the coastline of the National Park, we can continue by looking at a selection of places that I hope will give some flavour of the geology, landscapes and mining history of the inland part of the Park. This is necessarily a personal selection and I hope that I have not missed out too many of the places that you would have liked to see included.

DUNKERY BEACON AND DUNKERY GATE

I hesitated before including Dunkery Beacon (Plate 45) in the list of places to go, in view of the overpopularity of the place and the resulting path erosion problems. However, many visitors to the moor will probably want to climb to the highest point on Exmoor (1704 ft; 519 m) for the views alone, which can be magnificent. On a clear day you can see, for example, the Brecon Beacons in South Wales, Dartmoor, and Lundy Island.

There is a car park at Dunkery Gate [SS 895 406] from where the straightforward ascent to Dunkery Beacon can be made. The ridge is underlain by **Hangman Sandstone** which gives rise to the scatter of sandstone that you will see in the soil and in eroded tracks. At the top is a large cairn from where you can take in the views, using the Outdoor Leisure map to identify various features of the Exmoor landscape. Return to Dunkery Gate by the same route or pick a slightly different one from the map to reduce erosion.

You can see the junction between the **Hangman Sandstone** and the **Ilfracombe Slates** in the bed of the River Avill, below Dunkery Bridge. Below the bridge, the stream has cut down deeply and dramatically into the lowest part of the Ilfracombe Slates, which consists of grey and brownish grey **slates** and thin **siltstones**. You can also see **head**, especially above the bridge.

SIMONSBATH AREA

The village of Simonsbath (pronounced 'Simmunsbath') lies at the heart of an area of high moorland which was once the Royal Forest of Exmoor. The history of the 'reclamation' of Exmoor Forest by the Knight family of Simonsbath is a fascinating story which has been told by various authors (see the 'Further Reading' section at the end of the book). Amongst their many activities, the Knights, particularly Frederic Knight, made active attempts to exploit the iron ore of the area, without a great deal of success. For those of you interested in more detail of the mining history of the Forest, it has been dealt with in considerable detail in Orwin's book, in Roger Burton's book *The Heritage of Exmoor*, and in the booklet *Days of Renown* by J M Slader.

The northern part of the Forest, between Exe Plain and Elsworthy, is underlain by **Hangman Sandstone**, but the area between The Chains and around Simonsbath is underlain mainly by various slaty rocks, divisions of the **Ilfracombe Slates** and the

Plate 45. *A general view of Dunkery Beacon, looking north from Winsford Hill.*

Morte Slates. The boundary between the **Hangman Sandstone** and the **Ilfracombe Slates** can be seen by looking east from the B3223 road at a place [SS 756 413] near Exe Head Bridge (Plate 46). The valley of the River Exe runs more or less along the boundary.

The only extensive areas of upland **peat** within the National Park lie within Exmoor Forest, around The Chains and on Exe Plain and Lanacombe and, south-west of Simonsbath, around Burcombe, Squallacombe and Kinsford Gate.

It is curious that one of the highest parts of Exmoor, the prominent WNW-trending ridge

Plate 46. *The headwaters of the River Exe near Exe Head Bridge. The boundary between the Hangman Sandstone (to the left) and the Ilfracombe Slates (to the right) runs along the river valley.*

between Chapman Barrow and The Chains, should be formed of slates (**Ilfracombe Slates**) which would generally be regarded as being less resistant to weathering. One possible explanation is that the steeply dipping **cleavage** of the slates gives a greater resistance to erosion in contrast with the relatively low dips of bedding in the **Hangman Sandstone** to the north.

There are many possible walks through this beautiful landscape, some of which you can combine with visits to areas of mining or archaeological interest.

AROUND WARREN BRIDGE

The attractive valley of the River Exe around Warren Bridge, near Simonsbath, is worth a visit for its landscape features. There is access land west of the bridge, but the land east of the bridge is private. East of the bridge and on the north side of the valley, there are examples of **valley-floor knolls** (Plate 13) that can be seen from the public road down to Warren Bridge.

During the great Exmoor storm of 15 August 1952, which caused devastation in Lynmouth (see page 61), many **landslips** occurred along valley slopes on many parts of the Challacombe-Simonsbath area. They were also quite common on the south side of the Exe valley to the east and west of Warren Bridge. At the time of the storm, the landslip scars showed southward-dipping **slates** with **quartz veins** from top to bottom of the valley side. Most of these old landslip scars, now forty-five years old, have healed over, but they show how important extreme events such as the Exmoor storm, can be in changing the landscape quickly.

About a mile west of Warren Bridge, you can see Raven's Nest [SS 7777 4095], a north-facing hollow and cleft on the south side of the valley. It may have formed along a fault, but could also have been partly shaped by ice during the **Ice Age**.

There is another prominent example of a **valley-floor knoll** at Long Barrow in Exe Cleave, about a mile east of Warren Bridge. This feature is not a man-made burial chamber as the name suggests, but a natural feature developed in **Ilfracombe Slates** which are steeply inclined to the south.

About 1000 ft (300 m) east of Long Barrow there is more evidence of mining for iron. This is Honeymead Mine [SS 809 400], which consists of a very small surface working on the south side of the valley, and a **shaft** just south of the open workings.

A WALK TO WHEAL ELIZA

You can take a very pleasant walk along the River

Plate 47. *The remains of Wheal Eliza, a mine for iron and copper near Simonsbath.*

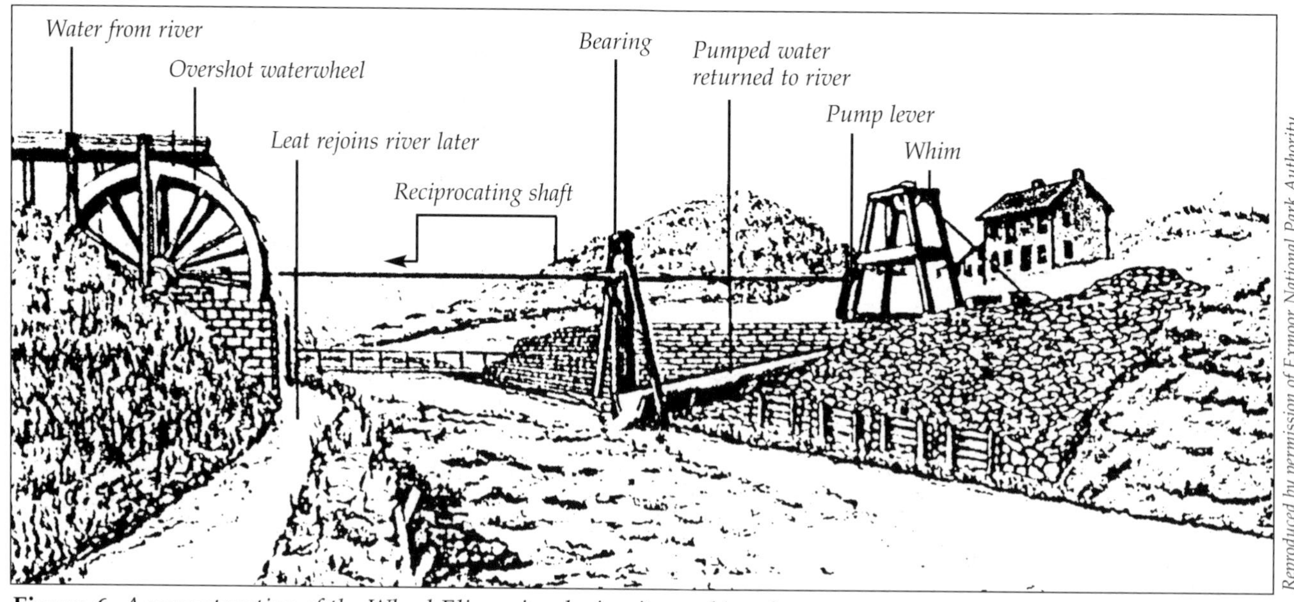

Figure 6. *A reconstruction of the Wheal Eliza mine during its working days.*

Barle from Simonsbath to the old mine workings at Wheal Eliza, beginning opposite the Exmoor Forest Hotel. The path is signposted to Wheal Eliza and Cow Castle. The first part of the walk takes you through Birchcleave Wood, a beech wood planted by the Knights. From the wood, continue along the path above the river, with prospects of Flexbarrow opening up ahead. Just beyond Flexbarrow you will find the sparse remains of Wheal Eliza, one of the Knights' less successful mining ventures, which was worked between 1846 and 1857. The mine is not typical of the district because copper and not iron was the main metal of interest. The mine buildings have now been almost totally demolished (Plate 47). Nearby you can see a **shaft** and small dumps.

Two parallel east-west **lodes** dipping at 75 degrees to the south were worked to a depth of 300 ft (91.4 m). On the dumps you will see iron ore, mainly **siderite**. You are much less likely to see scattered green secondary **copper** minerals and some primary **sulphides**.

On the opposite side of the river to the dumps you may be able to identify the remains of a wheel pit where a 25-ft (7.6-m) water wheel was once installed and worked pumps by flat rods across the river. The wheel took its water from a leat which leaves the River Barle just below Simonsbath. An artists impression of Wheal Eliza when working is shown in Figure 6.

Along the walk, you can see outcrops of **Ilfracombe Slates**, for example, beside the path just east of Flexbarrow (Plate 48).

The slates have been used in field walls, of which there are good examples on the eastern side of

Plate 48. *Ilfracombe Slates near Flexbarrow, Simonsbath.*

Flexbarrow, shown in Plate 18.

You could return to Simonsbath by the same route, or extend the walk, still following the River Barle, in order to see the Iron Age earthworks of Cow Castle, returning to Simonsbath via Picked Stones. The path takes you close to the dumps [SS 797 378] of Picked Stones Mine, last worked in 1914.

There are also attractive walks along the valley of the River Barle to Cow Castle and Wheal Eliza starting from the popular beauty spot at the medieval Landacre Bridge [SS 816 361].

CORNHAM FORD

You can see further evidence of mining activity in the Simonsbath area in combination with attractive walks to Cornham Ford, about one and a quarter miles west of Simonsbath. You can see dumps of iron ore (**hematite**) and **adits** down-river north-east of Cornham Ford [SS 749 386]. You can get there by various routes. One is along the River Barle from Simonsbath Bridge, a second from the Simonsbath-Challacombe road via Cornham Farm, and a third from the Simonsbath-North Molton road near Blue Gate [SS 758 377].

A good example of an early 'open-work' trench can be seen near Cornham Ford at [SS 7538]. It is about 700 yds (640 m) long and up to 26 ft (8 m) deep.

PINKWORTHY POND

Isolated bodies of water on moorland often provide a point of interest for walkers to aim for, and Pinkworthy Pond [SS 723 423] (pronounced 'Pinkery') in its setting amongst The Chains is no exception (Plate 49). You can reach it easily by footpath from the car park [SS 724 406] on the Simonsbath-Challacombe road. The pond is not a geological feature, but is man-made. It is sited on the **Ilfracombe Slates**, and you can see silty slates of this formation at the northern end of the pond. No one seems quite sure why the pond was built, but it may have been in connection with the construction of a proposed canal.

Photo courtesy of B.G.S.

Plate 49. *Pinkworthy Pond.*

You can still see the banks of a dry earthwork called the 'Pinkery Canal' which run along the contours on the southern slopes of The Chains from near Pinkworthy Ford [SS 724 423] to Exe Head [SS 752 413]. The purpose of the 'canal' is not clear but documents record the building of a 'water carriageway' (presumably the 'Pinkery Canal') on Goat Hill in 1833.

AROUND BRENDON HILL

The Brendon Hills, in the south-east of the National Park, were for a short time in the nineteenth century the centre of a thriving iron mining industry. I have given a short description of the industry in Chapter 4 of the book. Nowadays, you will have to look carefully for any signs of this past activity. However, although

Plate 50. *The cutting for the West Somerset Mineral Railway near Burrow Farm Mine.*

Plate 51. *The restored engine house of Burrow Farm Mine.*

Plate 52. *Robber's Bridge near Oareford.*

Photo courtesy of Mr H. C. Prudden.

Plate 53. *Valley-floor knolls along the Weir Water near Robber's Bridge.*

there are now few remaining surface buildings, such as engine houses, there are many old **adits** and **shafts** hidden away in the Brendons – 81 have been located. Please don't be tempted to enter any old workings if you find them, since most of them are extremely dangerous.

A WALK TO BURROW FARM ENGINE HOUSE ALONG THE WEST SOMERSET MINERAL RAILWAY

A visit to the restored **engine house** of one of the last of the Brendon Hill mines, at Burrow Farm, is an easy short walk. From Brendon Hill road junction take the Wheddon Cross road and turn left after about three-quarters of a mile. In about 200 yds (183 m) park on a lane verge near the interestingly named Naked Boy's Bridge [ST 014 344]. From here, you can walk westwards along a cutting which was dug for the West Somerset Mineral Railway (Plate 50) (see page 33 for more about this).

After about 600 yds (550 m), you can see the engine house and chimney of Burrow Farm Mine just south of the cutting. The existence of ancient workings in the area around Burrow Farm led the developers to hope for good quality ore at depth. As a result, a shaft for the mine was begun in 1860 and had reached a depth of 150 ft (45.7 m) by 1867. Enough ore was found to justify the cost of installing an engine in 1868, but the ore body was soon found to pinch out, and the mine closed in 1869. Another attempt was made in 1880, and another shaft was sunk about 400 yds (366 m) east of the engine house. You can still see some remains of it in the field. The new shaft had a short life, and the mine closed for good on 29 September 1883.

The engine house has been restored, and is the only remaining example of its type left on the Brendon Hills (Plate 51). The engine house at Kennisham Hill [SS 963 361], now regrettably demolished, was similar in appearance.

The resemblance of the Burrow Farm Mine engine house to many of those seen in Cornwall is striking, but not surprising in view of the fact that it was built by a Cornish mine captain, Henry Skewis. The rotary beam engine, 25 ft (7.6 m) in diameter, used steam generated in the boiler house by a coal-fired Lanark boiler. The ore needed no dressing and was hauled directly from the shaft in skips to the ore platform by the winding cable. The skips were pushed by hand along the platform and tipped into trucks which were then taken along the siding to join the West Somerset Mineral Railway for onward transport to the port of Watchet.

THE GREAT INCLINE

The remains of the Great Incline of the West Somerset Mineral Railway, by which iron ore was transferred from the Brendon Hill mines to the valley bottom at Comberow, are now unfortunately not easy to get at, and the only good impression of the scale of this great engineering structure can be gained from old photographs (Plate 16). About 530 yds (500 m) west of the Brendon Hill road junction, there are the ruins of the winding house at the top of the incline (Plate 17), but they are in a dangerous condition and should not be entered.

East of Brendon Hill, if you are an enthusiast for mine dumps, you may be interested to examine the **sideritic iron ore** on the dumps [ST 025 342] of Raleigh's Cross Mine, located on farmland just south of the Bampton road. However, the site is private, and you will need the farmer's permission for access.

Other old **shafts, adits** and dumps at Gupworthy [SS 966 353] are also on private land, and you will need to obtain permission to visit them.

BAMPFYLDE MINE

If you are interested in looking for minerals on mine dumps (having obtained the permission of the landowner first, of course), there are large dumps of copper-iron ores thrown out from Bampfylde Mine [SS 740 327] near Heasley Mill, North Molton. The dumps extend along the east bank of the River Mole where it turns to the east at a point about 600 yds (550 m) north of Heasley Mill. Typical vein material that has been found shows **vein quartz** with **hematite** or **siderite** and crystals, spots, veinlets and small lenses of **copper sulphides**. These are **chalcopyrite** and **bornite** which are altered in places to **covellite** and **chalcocite** and eventually to **malachite** and **azurite**.

Also, just west of the road there is an **adit** and poorly mineralised dumps extending up the side of the valley.

THE PUNCHBOWL

You can visit the interesting topographical feature of The Punchbowl [SS 882 344] easily from the car park [SS 878 341] on Winsford Hill, about four and a half miles NNW of Dulverton. Winsford Hill is itself an excellent viewpoint for the southern part of Exmoor and the Brendon Hills. The mounds on the hilltop are the Wambarrows, ancient burial mounds dating from the Bronze Age. The Punchbowl, sited on the **Pickwell Down Sandstones**, forms a distinctive steep-sided bowl-shaped feature opening to the north (Plate 7). Professor Straw (see Further Reading) has suggested that it may be an example of a hollow in which thick snow accumulated during cold phases of the **Ice Age**. It may even be the site of Exmoor's only **glacial corrie**.

ROBBER'S BRIDGE AND WEIR WATER

Robber's Bridge [SS 820 465] (Plate 52) is a popular beauty spot located near Oareford in the valley of the Weir Water. There is a large car park nearby, north of which you can see some scree on the steep slopes. You can see typical **Hangman Sandstone** in the stream bed near the bridge, consisting of purple fine-grained **sandstones** dipping generally eastwards. The bridge itself is made of the same type of sandstone. You can take a short walk upstream along the Weir Water to see some interesting **valley-floor knolls** (explained on page 27) on the north side of the valley. A good, somewhat more distant, viewpoint for these knolls (Plate 53) is from a place [SS 828 465] on Hookway Hill, the road that runs east from Robber's Bridge to join the main road at Oare Post. You can also see on the steep southern side of the valley two gulleys down which debris has been washed to form small debris cones at their base.

COUNTY GATE TO MALMSMEAD

A leaflet describing a geological walk from Malmsmead along the East Lyn valley, written by Hugh Prudden, is summarised here, but more detail is given in the leaflet. The walk, about 2 miles long, begins at the Malmsmead Field Centre. From there, turn left (north) off the road on to the public footpath, go over a footbridge and follow the river downstream on the east bank. In the river channel are **sandstones** belonging to the **Hangman Sandstone**. The path by the river eventually leads to fine examples of **scree** slopes on the north side of the valley [SS 791 486]. The screes are made up of angular pieces of hard sandstone. Continue up the zig-zag path to the Exmoor National Park Visitor Centre at County Gate. From there, return to Malmsmead along the footpath that runs along the side of the valley; you will probably see some more small areas of **Hangman Sandstone**.

CONSERVATION OF THE GEOLOGICAL HERITAGE OF EXMOOR

By D. Parsons and A. King, English Nature

Conservation is about sustaining the landscape and geological heritage of Exmoor for future generations to explore and enjoy. Together with their dependant ecosystems, we are entrusted with the long-term care of this unique, finite resource. The key to successful conservation is to ensure that the natural and cultural integrity of the moor is maintained and enhanced.

The framework used for conservation management is based on the Natural Areas approach. Natural Areas are tracts of land unified by their underlying geology, landforms and soils, which display characteristic types of vegetation and species of wildlife and support broadly similar patterns of land-use by man. The dependency of Natural Areas on underlying geology and geomorphological processes provides an opportunity to integrate wildlife and Earth heritage conservation, and so conserve the natural and cultural dimensions of the landscape. Exmoor and the Quantocks represent a single and distinctive Natural Area.

Exmoor National Park is underlain largely by Devonian rocks and contains several Sites of Special Scientific Interest (SSSIs). Those SSSIs designated for their Earth science interest by English Nature are shown in the table below. SSSIs are the best examples of our national heritage of wildlife habitats, geological features and landforms. They are protected by local planning control and the Wildlife and Countryside Act 1981 (as amended). The Earth heritage SSSI network represents England's protected national resource of preserved ancient environments through geological time. This resource must be conserved to maintain access to England's highly varied Earth heritage for future generations. The SSSIs of the National Park have a unique character and their statutory protection lies at the core of managing the conservation of Exmoor.

The main principle of conserving the geological SSSIs of the National Park depends whether they are 'exposure' or 'integrity' sites. The scientific or educational value of exposure sites lie in providing accessible exposures of an extensive deposit or structure which is otherwise concealed underground, for example, most quarries, cuttings, cliffs, outcrops and mines. Most of the Park's geological SSSIs, such as the marine Devonian Lynton Formation of the Watersmeet SSSI, are exposure-type sites. Management depends on maintaining exposure of fresh and weathered rock faces by, for example, quarrying or marine erosion. Integrity sites contain finite and limited deposits or landforms that are irreplaceable if destroyed. They are usually of limited lateral extent. The management of integrity sites, like the Pleistocene geomorphological features of the West Exmoor Coast and Woods SSSI, favours their preservation and restricts man-made changes. Removal of materials from integrity sites should be for scientific purposes only. The SSSIs of the National Park are not particularly fossiliferous and therefore are not vulnerable to the pressures of over-collecting of fossils. However, many sites around its periphery are rich in fossils and minerals and all who intend to collect should follow English Nature's 'Code of good practice' and the Code of Geological Fieldwork operated by the Geologists' Association. Obtaining legal title of ownership to your finds and sharing information with local Museums services are important aspects of collecting responsibly.

Park management plans and the influence of Local Agenda 21 support the conservation of Exmoor's landscape, culture and history and seek to maintain the biodiversity of this very special place. We all depend on the Earth's limited resources and must share them more fairly and care for them more wisely than we have done in the past. As the countryside of England continues to undergo major changes, with the loss of many natural areas to development, remaining areas, like Exmoor National Park are often under considerable pressure. Community programmes for local action aim to improve quality of life, enrich the quality of the local environment and work towards achieving more sustainable lifestyles. The preservation of Exmoor as a special area of natural beauty for our enjoyment is paramount.

Much of Exmoor National Park is privately owned and users should remember that by following the Country Code most areas can be enjoyed safely. The stewardship of the Park provided by the local landowners should be respected and permission for access sought wherever reasonably practicable.

SSSI name	Grid Reference	National Geological Interest
Dean Steep	SS 709479	Marine Devonian stratigraphy; *Lynton Formation* and *Hangman Sandstone Formation*
Glenthorne	SS 794499 - SS 805495	Non-marine Devonian stratigraphy; *Hangman Sandstone Formation*
North Exmoor	SS 770360 - SS 800430	Holocene (Flandrian) pollen stratigraphy
Watersmeet	SS 745487	Marine Devonian stratigraphy; *Lynton Formation*
West Exmoor Coast and Woods	SS 665495	Marine Devonian stratigraphy; *Lynton Formation* and *Hangman Sandstone Formation: Pleistocene geomorphology; dry valley and periglacial features*

Glossary

Adit. A nearly horizontal passage from the surface into a mine.

Alluvium. A general term for generally unconsolidated clay, silt, sand or gravel deposited by modern rivers or streams.

Ammonites. General term for a group of coiled fossils found especially in the **Jurassic**.

Anticline. A type of **fold** that is convex upwards.

Baggy Sandstones. A **Devonian formation** of North Devon, consisting mainly of **sandstones, siltstones** and **shales**.

Barite. A white, yellow or colourless mineral, barium sulphate. Distinguished by its heavy weight.

Bedding. The arrangement of **sedimentary** rocks in **beds** of different thickness and character (plate 54).

Beds. A layer in a **sedimentary** rock of generally uniform composition, separated from rocks above and below by more or less well defined boundaries (plate 54).

Bivalves. A type of fossil shell with two valves.

Photo courtesy of B.G.S.

Plate 54. *Bedding in the Hangman Sandstone just east of Hurlstone Point. Individual layers or beds are clearly defined as steep ledges in the cliff; these beds, orignally flat-lying, have been tilted by earth movements*

Black shales. A type of **shale** usually rich in organic material and formed in quiet, stagnant water.

Blue Lias. A **Jurassic formation** consisting of **shale** with **beds** of thin **limestone**.

Brachiopod (brack-ee-oh-pod). A type of fossil sea-shell.

Breccia (bretch-ee-ah). A type of **sedimentary** rock consisting of angular rock fragments cemented together.

Burrowing. The activity of organisms, such as worms, creating holes in soft **sediments** which may afterwards be filled with clay or sand.

Calcite. A common mineral, usually white, calcium carbonate. The main mineral in **limestones**.

Carboniferous. A geological period, between 355 and 298 million years old. Carboniferous rocks are widespread in central Devon, but not on Exmoor.

Chalcopyrite. A brass-yellow mineral, copper iron sulphate. One of the commonest **ores** of copper.

Chalk. A white, very fine-grained type of limestone, of **Cretaceous** age.

Cleavage. A property of fine-grained rocks, such as slates, by which they tend to split along closely spaced fractures caused by the alignment of 'platy' minerals.

Coastal waterfall. A type of waterfall which falls from the cliff top to the shore because the lower part of its valley has been left hanging by the erosional action of the sea.

Conglomerate (kon-glom-er-ayte). A type of coarse-grained **sedimentary** rock consisting of rounded rock fragments stuck together.

Convolute lamination. A type of **bedding,** usually in **sandstones** or **siltstone**, in which the layers are very crumpled and distorted, mainly by movements when the layers were still wet.

Corals. A marine organism that often forms colonies that make up coral reefs. Often quite common in **limestones**.

Cretaceous. A geological period covering the time between 135 and 65 million years ago.

Crinoid (cry-noyd). A type of marine organism with a stem and branches, sometimes known as a 'sea-lily'. Quite common in **limestones**.

Cupropyrite. A mineral containing copper and iron.

Delta. A triangular-shaped area of material deposited by a river at its mouth.

Devonian. A geological period, to which most of the rocks of Exmoor belong, covering the span of time between 405 and 355 million years ago.

Dip. The inclination of a layer in a rock, such as **bedding**, away from the horizontal.

Dip-and-scarp. A topographical feature consisting of a steep face ('scarp') and a less steep slope which is roughly parallel to the **dip** of the rocks beneath.

Engine house. The building that houses the pumping equipment by which water is pumped from a mine.

Erosion surface. A generally fairly level land surface which has been shaped by erosion, especially by running water.

Fans. A gently sloping fan-shaped accumulation of rock material, especially at the foot of steep slopes.

Fault. A fracture in a rock along which there has been some relative movement of the rock on either side.

Flint. A very fine-grained, hard, usually black form of silica, often occurring as nodules in the **Chalk**, and also often found reworked into river gravels.

Flood-plain. The flat area along the floor of a river valley which may become covered with water if the river overflows its banks. It is underlain by **alluvium**.

Fold. A curve or a bend in the layers of a rock, usually caused by the rock being subject to pressure. Hence **folding** and **folded** (plate 55).

Formation. A body of rocks of generally similar type which can be shown on a geological map.

Galena. A very heavy, shiny silvery-grey mineral, lead sulphide. It commonly contains traces of silver, as in the Combe Martin area.

Photo courtesy of B.G.S.

Plate 55. *Folds in the Hangman Sandstone near Hurlstone Point. Earth movements have crumpled the sandstone into a series of undulations.*

Geological time scale. A chronological arrangement of the sequence of geological events.

Glacial corrie. A bowl-shaped hollow on the side of a hill or mountain produced by the erosional action of a mountain **glacier**. Sometimes called a cirque.

Glaciation(s). The covering of large land areas by **glaciers** or **ice sheets**. Several episodes of glaciation have occurred over the last two million years.

Glacier. A large mass of ice which creeps downslope and commonly fills valleys.

Goethite. A yellowish, reddish or brownish black iron oxide mineral.

Granite. An **igneous** rock found, in South West England, on Dartmoor, Bodmin Moor etc.

Ham Hill Stone. A type of **Jurassic limestone** found near Yeovil, Somerset.

Hangman Sandstone. A **Devonian formation** of North Devon, consisting mainly of purple, grey and green **sandstones** and some **siltstones, shales** and **slates**, with minor amounts of **conglomerate**.

Head. Locally derived angular rubble formed by downslope movement as a result of freezing and thawing of material in a cold climate.

Hematite. A common iron oxide mineral, dark grey to reddish brown in colour.

Hog's-back cliff. A type of cliff with a long seaward slope above a rather small seacliff at the base of the slope.

Ice Age. A term used to cover the period of **glaciations** over the last two million years.

Ice cap. A dome shaped mass of ice covering an upland area, smaller in size than an ice sheet.

Ice sheet. A mass of ice of generally continental size.

Igneous (ig-knee-us) A type of rock that has solidified from originally molten material.

Ilfracombe Slates. A **Devonian formation** of North Devon, consisting mainly of **slates** with some **limestones** and minor amounts of **sandstones**.

Interglacial. The intervals between periods of **glaciation**.

Joints. A fracture in a rock along which no displacement has occurred (plate 56).

Jurassic. A period of geological time spanning the time between 205 and 135 million years ago. Named after the Jura Mountains between France and Switzerland.

Landslips. Areas of soil and rock material which have moved downslope fairly rapidly.

Lime. Calcium oxide, produced by the burning of **limestone**, calcium carbonate. Used in agriculture.

Limekiln. A structure in which limestone was burnt to form **lime.**

Plate 56. *Joints in the Hangman Sandstone at Greenaleigh. A fold is a cut by well-defined near-vertical fractures.*

Limestone. A **sedimentary rock** made up mainly of calcium carbonate. There are many different types, some of which contain fossils.

Limonite. A generally brown iron oxide mineral.

Luccombe Breccia. A type of ancient gravel and sandstone, probably of **Triassic** age, made up of angular pieces of **sandstone** and **slate**. Occurs around the village of Luccombe in the Vale of Porlock.

Lynton Formation. A **Devonian formation** of North Devon, consisting mainly of **slates** and **sandstones**.

Marl. A clay or **mudstone** with some content of calcium carbonate, and therefore useful for liming soils.

Mercia Mudstone. The group name for a number of geological **formations** of **Triassic** age, which are mainly red **mudstones**, with some grey mudstones near the top. Minor sandstones may also occur.

Mineralisation. The process by which minerals are introduced into rocks, resulting in economically or potentially valuable deposits.

Morte Slates. A **Devonian formation** of North Devon, consisting mainly of grey slates.

Mudstone. A type of **sedimentary rock** consisting of indurated mud, generally rather blocky and massive in appearance.

New Red Sandstone. A general name for all the mainly red **conglomerates, breccias, sandstones** and **mudstones** of **Permian** and **Triassic** age in South-West England. Distinguished from the **Old Red Sandstone** of **Devonian** age.

Old Red Sandstone. A general term for rocks of **Devonian** age, especially red **sandstones** and **mudstones**, deposited on a desert continent stretching from South Wales to Scotland.

Oligocene (oll-ig-oh-seen). A period of the Tertiary era, covering the time from 34 to 23 million years ago.

Ore. A rock or mineral rich enough in metal to be worth working.

Peat. Partly carbonized vegetable matter formed in bogs and sometimes cut for fuel.

Permian (Perm-ee-an). A period of geological time, covering the period from 298 to 251 million years ago. Not known for certain to occur on Exmoor.

Pickwell Down Sandstones. A **Devonian formation** of North Devon, consisting mainly of purple and brown **sandstones** and **shales**.

Pilton Shales. A **formation** of North Devon which spans the boundary between the **Devonian** and the **Carboniferous**. It consists mainly of **shales** with **sandstones** and calcareous sandstones and thin limy lenses.

Precambrian. the period of geological time from the beginning of the Cambrian 570 million years ago to the beginning of the Earth at about 4 600 million years ago. It is therefore equivalent to about 90 percent of geological time.

Pyrite. A common brass-yellow mineral, iron sulphide.

Quartz. An extremely common mineral, colourless or commonly white, but may be many colours. Silicon oxide. It is the commonest valueless part of an **ore**.

Quartz veins. A fracture in a rock filled with the mineral **quartz**.

Quaternary. The span of time covering the last two million years.

Raised beach. Ancient beach occurring above the present shoreline, generally indicating lowering of sea level since it was formed.

Ripple marks. Small alternating parallel ridges and hollows found in some **sedimentary** rocks, especially **sandstone**, and formed either on land (by wind), or in water (by currents) (plate 57).

River gravel. Gravel moved and deposited by the action of water in rivers.

River terrace. A flat-topped surface overlying a deposit, usually gravel, and representing the dissected remains of earlier **alluvium**.

Saltmarsh deposits. Deposits of salt marshes, formed in poorly drained coastal areas subject to occasional flooding by salt water. Mainly consisting of mud and occasional peat. Found east of Minehead and in the Vale of Porlock.

Photo courtesy of Mr H. C. Prudden

Plate 57. *Ripple marks on a slab of Hangman Sandstone.*

Sandstone. A type of **sedimentary** rock, composed of sand-sized grains cemented together.

Scree. Angular **sandstone** rubble forming on steep valley sides (plate 58).

Sedimentary. Said of a type of rock formed of two main types: first, made up of fragments worn from pre-existing rocks and laid down either in water or on land, and including **shales, mudstones, sandstones, conglomerates** and **breccias**. Secondly, formed from solution, mainly in the sea, and including **limestones**. Sedimentary rocks are typically layered.

Plate 58. *Scree slopes in Parsonage Cleave, near Malmsmead.*

Sediments. The materials that eventually become **sedimentary** rocks.

Shaft. A vertical tunnel constructed in a mine to carry **ore**, men and materials up and down to the mining levels, or for ventilation.

Shale. A type of **sedimentary** rock formed by the induration of mud, and distinguished from mudstone by the property of splitting along the **bedding**.

Shingle ridge. A narrow beach of pebbles and cobbles piled up by storm waves (plate 59).

Siderite. An iron carbonate mineral, yellowish brown, brownish red or brownish black, one of the main ores of the Brendon Hills Iron Ore Field.

Sideritic iron ore. A type of **ore** mainly made up of **siderite**.

Siltstone. A type of **sedimentary** rock made up of cemented-together silt-sized grains.

Slate. A type of rock formed under heat and pressure

Plate 59. *The shingle ridge at Porlock Bay, looking towards Hurlstone Point in the far distance.*

from **shale** or **mudstone** causing the platy minerals in the rock to align and create a **cleavage** along which the rock splits easily.

Slickensides. A polished and scratched surface caused by friction along a **fault**.

Spathic ore. An old term for **sideritic iron ore**.

Sphalerite. A usually brown or black zinc and iron sulphide mineral.

Subaerial. Forming on a land surface, for example by the action of rivers.

Submerged forest. The remains of an ancient forest now found at low tide or below sea level, indicating a relative rise in sea level since its formation.

Sulphides. A mineral compound in which sulphur is linked to a metal, for example **galena**, lead sulphide.

Syncline. A **fold**, which is concave upwards.

Terminal curvature. Downslope bending of **bedding** or **cleavage** close to the ground surface, caused by downhill creep of the upper layers.

Tertiary. The first period of the Cainozoic era, covering the time span from about 65 to 2 million years ago.

Trace-fossil. A structure in **sedimentary** rocks resulting from the activities of an animal – for example, a track, trail or burrow.

Triassic. A period of geological time covering the period from 251 to 205 million years ago. Present in the eastern part of Exmoor National Park around Porlock, Wootton Courtenay and Minehead

Tufa. A chemical **sedimentary** rock, a type of **limestone** deposited from solution by springs.

Umber. A naturally occurring dark brown earth, used as a paint pigment, and formed near Combe Martin by weathering of **limestones** in the **Ilfracombe Slates**.

Upcott Slates. A Devonian **formation** of North Devon. It consists mainly of buff, grey-green and purple **slates**.

Valley-floor knolls. Upstanding ridges and knolls of rock along a valley floor.

Vein. A fracture in a rock filled with **ore** minerals.

Vein quartz. Quartz derived from **quartz veins**.

Wave-cut platform. A roughly horizontal surface produced by wave erosion.

Further Reading

GENERAL

Binding, H. (editor), 1995. *The Changing Face of Exmoor.* (Tiverton: Exmoor Books).

Blackmore, R. D., *Lorna Doone.*

Burton, R. A., 1989. *The Heritage of Exmoor.* (Tiverton: Roger A Burton).

Burton, S. H., 1984. *Exmoor.* (London: Robert Hale).

Court, G., *Exmoor National Park.* (London: Webb & Bower).

Crabtree, K., and Maltby, E., 1974. 'Soil and land use on Exmoor: significance of a buried profile on Exmoor.' *Proceedings of the Somersetshire Archaeological and Natural History Society*, Vol. 119, 38-43. ['Pinkery Canal'].

Orwin, C. S., and Sellick, R. J., 1972. *The Reclamation of Exmoor Forest.* (Newton Abbot: David & Charles).

Peel, J. H. B., 1970. *Portrait of Exmoor.* (London: Robert Hale).

GEOLOGY

Durrance, E. M., and Laming, D. J. C., (editors). 1982. *The Geology of Devon* (Exeter: University of Exeter).

Edmonds, E. A., McKeown, and Williams, M., 1975. *British Regional Geology. South-West England* (Fourth edition). (London: HMSO).

Edmonds, E. A., Whittaker, A., and Williams, B. J., 1985. *Geology of the country around Ilfracombe and Barnstaple.* Memoir of the British Geological Survey, geological sheets 277 and 293. (London: HMSO).

Edwards, R.A., 1999. *The Minehead district – A concise account of the geology.* Memoir of the British Geological Survey, geological sheet 278 and part of sheet 294. (London: The Stationery Office).

Evans, J. W,. 1922. 'The geological structure of the country around Combe Martin, North Devon'. *Proceedings of the Geologists' Association,* Vol. 33, 201-228.

Binding, H., for Exmoor National Park, 1993. *Geology on Exmoor.* Filex 4. [Leaflet].

Horner, L., 1816. 'Sketch of the geology of the south-western part of Somerset'. *Transactions of the Geological Society of London*, Vol. 3, 338-384.

Scrivener, R. C., and Bennett, M. J., 1980. 'Ore genesis and controls of mineralisation in the Upper Palaeozoic rocks of North Devon'. *Proceedings of the Ussher Society*, Vol. 5, 54-58.

Webby, B. D., 1965. 'The stratigraphy and structure of the Devonian rocks in the Brendon Hills, West Somerset'. *Proceedings of the Geologists' Association*, vol. 76, 39-60.

THE SHAPE OF EXMOOR

Allen, N. V., 1978. *The Waters of Exmoor.* (Dulverton: Exmoor Press).

Arber, E. A. N., 1911. *The Coast Scenery of North Devon.* (London: Dent). [Facsimile edition 1969, Kingsmead Reprints, Bath].

Dalzell, D., and Durrance, E. M., 1980. 'The evolution of the Valley of Rocks'. *Transactions of the Institute of British Geographers.* No. 5, 66-79.

Gifford, J., 1953. II.- 'Landslides on Exmoor caused by the storm of 15th August, 1952'. *Geography*, Vol. 38, 9-17.

Keene, P., and Elsom, D., 1990. *Lyn in Flood, Watersmeet to Lynmouth.* (Oxford Brookes University, Thematic Trails No. 11).

Keene, P., and Pearce, B., 1993. *Valley of Rocks, Lynton.* (Oxford Brookes University, Thematic Trails No. 12).

Simpson, S., 1953. 'The development of the Lyn drainage system and its relation to the origin of the coast between Combe Martin and Porlock'. *Proceedings of the Geologists' Association*, Vol. 64, 14-23.

Straw, A., 1995. 'Aspects of the geomorphology of Exmoor'. 13-25 in Binding, H. (editor). *The Changing Face of Exmoor.* (Tiverton: Exmoor Books).

Wilson, H., 1995. 'The coastal geomorphology of Exmoor. 26-32 in Binding, H. (editor). *The Changing Face of Exmoor'*. (Tiverton: Exmoor Books).

MINING AND RAILWAYS

Bryant, T C., 1980. 'The Hollow Hills of Brendon'. *Wessex Cave Club Journal*, Vol. 16, No. 180, 7-14. [List of mine entrances in the Brendon Hills. An addendum in 1985 (*Wessex Cave Club Journal*, Vol. 18, No. 204, p. 78) listed three more entrances in the Eisen Hill area in addition to the 78 already listed].

Dines, H. G., 1956. 'The metalliferous mining region of south-west England'. *Memoir of the Geological Survey of Great Britain.*

Sellick, R., 1970. *The West Somerset Mineral Railway and the story of the Brendon Hills iron mines.* (Newton Abbot: David & Charles).

Slader, J. M., 1965. *Days of Renown. The story of mining on Exmoor and the border parishes.* West Country Handbook No. 6 (Bracknell: West Country Handbooks).

Stuckey, D., 1965. *Adventurers' slopes. The story of the silver and other mines of Combe Martin in Devon.* West Country Handbook No. 7 (Bracknell: West Country Handbooks).

QUARRYING

Tilley, C., 1992. 'The West Somerset slate industry'. *Bulletin of the Somerset Industrial Archaeology Society*, No. 61, 20-24.

Warren, D. W., 1977. 'Newland Quarry'. *Somerset Industrial Archaeological Society Journal*, Vol. 2, 36-39.

ARCHAEOLOGY

Atkinson, M., (editor). 1997. *Exmoor's Industrial Archaeology.* (Tiverton: Exmoor Books).

Eardley-Wilmot, H., 1983. *Ancient Exmoor.* (Dulverton: Exmoor Press).

Grinsell, L. V., 1970. *The Archaeology of Exmoor*. (Newton Abbot: David & Charles).

WALKING GUIDES

Conduit, B., (compiler). 1990. *Exmoor and the Quantocks walks.* (Norwich: Ordnance Survey/Jarrold).

Earle, J., 1991. *Exmoor and the Quantocks. A walker's guide.* (Milnthorpe, Cumbria: Cicerone Press).

Exmoor National Park Authority. 1991. *Walks from Combe Martin. Silver mines.* [Leaflet].

Gunnell, C., 1981. *Somerset and North Devon Coast Path.*

National Trust. *Watersmeet & Countisbury.* [Booklet including four walks].

National Trust. *The West Exmoor coast.* [Booklet including four walks].

National Trust. *Explore Holnicote.* [Booklet].

CONSERVATION

Nature Conservancy Council (now English Nature). 1990 & 1991. *Earth science conservation in Great Britain - A strategy.*

English Nature. 1992. *Fossil collecting and conservation.* [Leaflet].

Nature Conservancy Council (now English Nature). 1991. *Conserving our heritage of Rocks, Fossils and Landforms.* [Leaflet].

Nature Conservancy Council (now English Nature). 1990. *Regionally Important Geological/geomorphological Sites.* [Leaflet].

English Nature. 1991. *Earth science conservation for Farmers and Landowners.* [Leaflet].

English Nature. 1997. *Windows in Time – Earth heritage and Local Nature Reserves.* [Booklet].

English Nature. 1995. *Conserving England's Earth Heritage.* [Pamphlet].

Countryside Commission, English Heritage and English Nature. 1995. *Ideas into Action for Local Agenda 21.*